BBC Speakout
3RD EDITION

B2

Workbook

Pearson Education Limited
KAO Two
KAO Park
Hockham Way
Harlow, Essex
CM17 9SR
England
and Associated Companies throughout the world.

pearsonenglish.com/speakout3e

© Pearson Education Limited 2022

All rights reserved; no part of this publication may be reproduced, stored in a retrieval system, or transmitted in any form or by any means, electronic, mechanical, photocopying, recording, or otherwise without the prior written permission of the Publishers.

First published 2022

ISBN: 978-1-292-40735-7

Set in BBC Reith Sans

Printed in Slovakia by Neografia

Acknowledgements
Written by Helen Chilton

Image Credit(s):
Getty Images: 10'000 Hours/DigitalVision 32, BeyondImages/E+ 14, CSA Images/Vetta 27, Drazen/E+ 37, Eduardo Fonseca Arraes/Moment 12, FatCamera/E+ 49, fotografixx/iStock 13, Jim Craigmyle/Stone 54-55, Jonathan Knowles/Stone 9, Karen Schuld/Tetra images 25, katleho Seisa/E+ 11, Klaus Vedfelt/DigitalVision 18, MoMo Productions/DigitalVision 51, Monty Rakusen/Image Source 47, Peter Muller/Image Source 35, Richard Bailey/Corbis 33, skynesher/E+ 41, suteishi/E+ 23, Tara Moore/DigitalVision 33, Tim Robberts/DigitalVision 33, timandtim/Digital Vision 7, Westend61 33

Cover Images: Front: **Alamy Stock Photo:** Westend61 GmbH; **Getty Images:** adamkaz, Hinterhaus Productions, We Are

Illustrated by: Rupert Van Wyk (Beehive Illustration): 21

CONTENTS

LESSON	VOCABULARY	GRAMMAR	PRONUNCIATION
1A pp4–5	personality adjectives; suffixes	present perfect simple and continuous	weak forms of *have* and *been*
1B pp6–7	collocations about memory; idioms: memory	infinitive and *-ing* forms	chunking: two-part collocations
1C | 1D pp8–9	emotions and feelings	*while*, *whereas* and *whilst*	word stress: dependent propositions
2A pp10–11	science and technology; word families	future probability	connected speech: future probability
2B pp12–13	nature	quantifiers	connected speech: quantifiers
2C | 2D pp14–15	lifestyle adjectives; extreme adjectives		stress to show certainty
REVIEW 1–2 pp16–17			
3A pp18–19	festivals; the environment	relative clauses	pitch in non-defining relative clauses
3B pp20–21	phrasal verbs: performing; phrasal verbs: communication	cleft sentences	emphatic stress
3C | 3D pp22–23	film and TV	*do* and *did* for emphasis	linking and elision
4A pp24–25	health and lifestyle; illness and treatment	future continuous and future perfect	connected speech: future perfect
4B pp26–27	sleep	passives	sentence stress: content and function words
4C | 4D pp28–29	exercise; sport: motivation and benefits; phrases related to time		stress in phrases for partial agreement
REVIEW 3–4 pp30–31			
5A pp32–33	time expressions	past perfect simple and continuous	connected speech: past perfect continuous
5B pp34–35	work and careers; areas of work	past plans and intentions	connected speech: intrusive /w/ sounds
5C | 5D pp36–37	video conference calls	non-defining relative clauses for comments	intonation to show degrees of certainty
6A pp38–39	prefixes	necessity, prohibition and permission	word stress: prefixes
6B pp40–41	reporting verbs	reported orders, requests and advice	consonant clusters
6C | 6D pp42–43	collocations with *get* and *take*; fillers		pitch for sounding tactful
REVIEW 5–6 pp44–45			
7A pp46–47	compound adjectives; chance	past modals of deduction	connected speech: in past modals of deduction
7B pp48–49	idioms: regrets	*wish, if only, should have*	chunking in idioms
7C | 7D pp50–51	phrasal verbs: explaining	adverbials of concession	stress in phrasal verbs
8A pp52–53	collocations with *go, have* and *make*; describing homes and living conditions	participle clauses	pitch in participle clauses
8B pp54–55	world issues	conditionals with conjunctions	stress in conditional sentences
8C | 8D pp56–57	prepositional phrases; phrases with *get*		sounding persuasive
REVIEW 7–8 pp58–59			

CUMULATIVE REVIEW 1–4 pp60–61	CUMULATIVE REVIEW 5–8 pp62–63	CUMULATIVE REVIEW 1–8 pp64–67
AUDIOSCRIPTS pp68–77	**ANSWER KEY** pp78–94	

Lesson 1A

GRAMMAR | present perfect simple and continuous
VOCABULARY | personality adjectives; suffixes
PRONUNCIATION | weak forms of *have* and *been*

VOCABULARY

personality adjectives

1 A Choose the correct word to complete the sentences.

1 He's so _____! He's planning to open two new restaurants by the end of the year.
   a adventurous   b ambitious   c hopeful

2 Hilda is the most _____ person I know. She seems to disagree with everything I say.
   a argumentative   b rebellious   c stubborn

3 People often go through a _____ stage of life, where they want to break rules.
   a rebellious   b curious   c stubborn

4 I think I'm pretty _____. I've climbed a mountain, trekked through the Amazon – that kind of thing.
   a outgoing   b stubborn   c adventurous

5 My sister's very _____. Once she's made her mind up, she won't change it.
   a outgoing   b stubborn   c argumentative

6 My twin brother and I are completely different. I'm quite shy, whereas he's very _____.
   a rebellious   b ambitious   c outgoing

B Complete the conversation with the adjectives in the box.

adventurous   ambitious   argumentative
cheerful   curious   outgoing   rebellious
stubborn

A: Do you get on well with your brother and sister?
B: Usually, but my brother can be a bit ¹_____. Whatever my opinion is, he'll almost always tell me I'm wrong. He's quite ²_____, too. He never follows rules and sometimes gets in trouble at school.
A: Oh, dear! Your sister's always very ³_____. She seems to enjoy life.
B: Yeah, she does. She's quite ⁴_____ and has got loads of friends. I'm quieter than her. Anyway, what about you and your brother?
A: We get on fine. He's a lot older than me, so he's working now. He's quite ⁵_____. Like, he's already going for a promotion.
B: He sounds quite ⁶_____, as well. Doesn't he go mountain climbing?
A: Yeah, he's very ⁷_____ about the world – wants to know everything and try everything.
B: I wish my brother was more like yours!
A: Oh, he isn't perfect. He can be very ⁸_____ and won't change his mind for anything!

suffixes

2 Complete the sentences with the adjective form of the words in brackets.

1 Our new teacher's really _____ (help) – she sent a list of useful websites to the group.
2 I'm not _____ (art) at all. I can't even draw simple objects.
3 Wow! That musician was so _____ (talent)! Imagine being able to play the piano like that.
4 I'm quite an _____ (emotion) person – I always cry at the end of films.
5 I think you need to be more _____ (realist). Can you really be a professional footballer?
6 Jade isn't very _____ (like). She says unpleasant things about people behind their backs.
7 Rupert is an _____ (experience) lawyer with over 30 years in the industry.

GRAMMAR

present perfect simple and continuous

3 A Choose the correct word or phrase to complete the sentences.

1 I've **called** / **been calling** / **'m calling** the doctor's all morning, but no one's answering.
2 Have you **had** / **having** / **been having** your hair cut? It's looks great!
3 Felix has **been** / **had** / **been having** lessons recently and is making great progress so far.
4 How many times have you **visited** / **been visiting** / **been** Canada?
5 I've **studied** / **study** / **been studying** Japanese for just over a year now.
6 She's **raised** / **been raising** / **raising** €1,000 for charity.

B Complete the blog post using the correct form of the verbs in brackets.

Something I'm working on

Ellie Behr | Fri 23 Oct | 10.27 GMT

Regular followers of my blog will know that, I ¹_____ always _____ (be) a shy, quiet person who hates conflict and walks away from any kind of argument. Recently, though, I ²_____ (work) on being more assertive, by which I mean being stronger and more confident. I ³_____ (have) three sessions with a life coach, who ⁴_____ (help) me to finally understand that being assertive is not the same as being aggressive, and that people have more respect for you when you stand up for yourself. Recently, I ⁵_____ (practise) the things we've talked about and it ⁶_____ (be) a real eye-opener!

1A

C Use the prompts to write present perfect simple or present perfect continuous sentences.
1 I / see / that new Wes Anderson film / five times now.
2 You / work / on that report / all morning!
3 Have / you go / anywhere interesting recently?
4 Ben / never try / horse-riding / because he / scared of horses!
5 He / take / a year off / go travelling.
6 I / look / for you / the last half an hour!

PRONUNCIATION

4 A 🔊 1.01 | weak forms of *have* and *been* | Listen and choose the correct words to complete the sentences.
1 **He's never been** / **She's never been** to Poland.
2 How long **have you been** / **have they been** studying in Manchester?
3 What's **he been** / **she been** up to this week?
4 **They've been** / **I've been** trying to book flights to Mexico all morning.
5 **She's been** / **He's been** waiting here for the last four hours.

B 🔊 1.01 | Listen again and repeat.

LISTENING

5 A 🔊 1.02 | Listen to an interview about identity. Put the topics in the order they are discussed.
 a Other factors that influence our identity
 b How to find yourself
 c The elements that form our identity
 d How we develop our sense of self
 e The importance of self-identity

B 🔊 1.02 | Listen to the interview again. Complete the sentences with no more than three words from the recording.
1 Identity is a combination of your _____, your likes and dislikes, your moral code and what motivates you.
2 Without a clear sense of self, it can be difficult to _____.
3 Parents provide _____ for how their children should behave.
4 Your identity isn't _____ – it develops over the course of your life.
5 Our relationships and experiences _____ our sense of self.

C 📝 🔊 1.03 | Listen to the speaker's final advice again and write what you hear. You will hear the sentence only once.

_____
_____

WRITING

a blog post

6 A Read the blog post. How has the writer changed? Complete the summary with words from the text.

I'm not the person I once was

When I was a young kid, I was pretty adventurous. I was always out in the woods near home, climbing trees and swimming in the river. As a teenager, I was a bit of a risk-taker and didn't think twice about the stuff I did: snowboarding, sky-diving, you name it! I think I've changed considerably since then. These days I much prefer indoor activities and I've been a music teacher for the last four years. I've become a lot calmer as a result! I'm still curious about the world, but I haven't done anything 'extreme' for a long time!

I'm definitely less ¹_____ and no longer a ²_____. Nowadays, ³_____ are more my thing, and my role as a ⁴_____ has calmed me down. That doesn't mean I'm not ⁵_____ about what's going on around me. I just choose not to take part in ⁶_____ sports like snowboarding and sky-diving anymore!

B Read the comments. Underline examples of the present perfect simple and continuous.

Astrid94
14.07 | 2 Nov

I would say that I've actually changed very little. I've always been very close to my family and we agree on most things. You'll often find us all on the golf course, too – recently I've taken up the sport so I can join my parents and brothers for a game!

JosephER
14.22 | 2 Nov

I've changed loads! As a young child I was quiet like my mum, who brought me up on her own, but in my teenage years I was rebellious and hated school with a passion. I think I've outgrown that, and I've been channelling my energy into being ambitious instead.

I_Kara
14:39 | 2 Nov

I've always had two sides to my personality. In my work as a gym instructor, I'm patient and cheerful, but in my personal life, I'm a total stress-head, though I've been working on that! I still love nothing more than getting together with friends and debating all the issues important to us.

C Make notes about how these things have changed as you have got older. Then write a blog post. Write 100–140 words.
• your personality
• your interests
• your values

Lesson 1B

GRAMMAR | infinitive and -ing forms
VOCABULARY | collocations about memory; idioms: memory
PRONUNCIATION | chunking: two-part collocations

VOCABULARY

collocations about memory

1 Choose the correct word or phrase to complete the sentences.

1 I **remember every detail** / **learn things by heart** / **brought back memories** of that day – the sunlight on my pillow, the smell of my mother's cooking downstairs …
2 My **short-term** / **long-term** / **perfect recall** memory is terrible. I can't even remember what I had for breakfast!
3 You need to learn your lines by **recall** / **memory** / **heart** when you're acting on stage.
4 Oh, that programme **remembered every detail** / **brought back memories** / **had a good memory** for me. I used to work in the building that was featured in it.
5 What are your earliest **long-term** / **short-term** / **childhood** memories?
6 I haven't **brought** / **got** / **learned** a good memory – I never remember anything!

idioms: memory

2 A Match the idioms (1–6) with the sentences which have a similar meaning (a–f).

1 Things go in one ear and out the other.
2 It slipped my mind.
3 Can you refresh my memory?
4 It's on the tip of my tongue.
5 That rings a bell.
6 My memory's playing tricks on me.

a It sounds familiar.
b I forgot.
c I quickly forget.
d I've remembered that incorrectly.
e I can't quite remember it!
f Please remind me.

B Complete the sentences with the correct form of the idioms in the box.

in one ear and out the other
memory is playing tricks on me
on the tip of my tongue   refresh my memory
rings a bell   slip my mind

1 Now, what was it? No, don't tell me – it's ....
2 That name definitely .... Did she used to work here?
3 I thought I'd sent that already. I guess my ....
4 Now, ... – what time are we starting tomorrow again?
5 You never listen! Honestly, it all goes ....
6 I forgot the milk! Sorry, it totally ....

PRONUNCIATION

3 A 🔊 1.04 | **chunking: two-part collocations** | Listen and complete the sentences.

1 My .... is better than my ....
2 I've got .... when it comes to phone numbers!
3 This song brings back a lot of ....

B 🔊 1.04 | Listen again and repeat.

GRAMMAR

infinitive and -ing forms

4 A Choose the correct words to complete the sentences.

1 I think the plan is **to meet** / **meeting** Max outside the venue.
2 Annoyingly, he forgot **to set** / **setting** a timer and burnt the dinner.
3 I remember **to get up** / **getting up** early and watching TV.
4 No, he stopped **to go** / **going** to Spanish classes last month.
5 Mum rang – she wants **to have** / **having** dinner with you tonight.
6 Remember **to lock** / **locking** the door when you leave.

B Complete the anecdote with the correct form of the verbs in brackets.

As a child, my primary goal was [1] .... (climb) the really big mountain I could see from my bedroom window. I did some exercise every day – which involved running up and down the stairs – [2] .... (improve) my stamina, so I could make the climb.

Then, one morning, I remember [3] .... (set off) with some sandwiches in my schoolbag, announcing to my dad I'd be back in time for dinner after my day's climbing. I walked and walked, and eventually turned back so as [4] .... (make sure) I was home before dark. I was tired and looking forward to [5] .... (have) a big bowl of soup.

In reality, I'd only been gone an hour, with my dad trailing me from a distance. The whole family still laugh about my adventure – but I'm going to try [6] .... (reach) the top of that mountain one day!

READING

5 A Skim the article and tick the topics that are mentioned.
1. What happens in the brain
2. How we adapt stories to our audience
3. How and why we adapt stories
4. Why we forget things
5. What the research tells us
6. How people experience things differently

B Scan the article again and underline the following information.
1. Why our memories are useful to us
2. Why we make minor changes every time we tell a story
3. What we call memories that are entirely invented
4. The name for the process of changing our memory according to who we're talking to
5. What we do when we can't remember something

C Read the article again choose the correct option (a–c).
1. What does the writer say in the second paragraph?
   a We often change stories that we think make us look bad.
   b We may or may not be aware that we are adapting our stories.
   c We usually know how someone will react to a story.
2. What point does the writer make in the fourth paragraph?
   a Despite changes, memories are likely to be relatively accurate.
   b We invent more 'facts' each time we recall a memory.
   c A memory becomes what we last described it to be.
3. What would make the best alternative title for the article?
   a How our memories change as we get older
   b Your memory may not be as good as you think it is
   c Why it is sometimes difficult to remember things

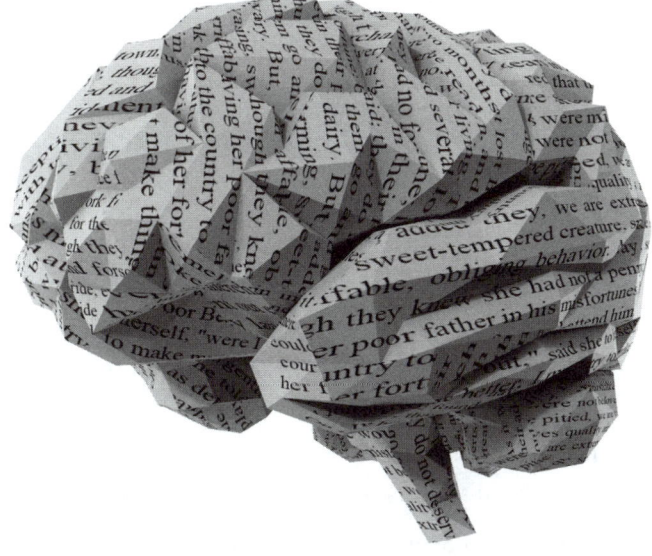

Why you can't trust your own memory

Ayodele Odetoyinbo | Mon 27 Jun

Have you got a good memory? If you answered 'yes', then you might want to think again. Research has shown that our memories may not be as reliable as we think. Since our memories help us recall past events, learn from our mistakes and play a part in creating our identities, this may not be the best news!

When we describe something that has happened to us, we often make tiny adjustments each time we tell it, without even realising we're doing it. The reason for this could be because we wish that what we are saying is true, or we want our listener to think in a particular way about what we're telling them. For example, we might want to make them laugh or feel sorry for us – in which case, we may make changes consciously. When we recall the story again in the future, it is likely to be rather different to what we really experienced.

And think about those times when you were with friends and you experienced something amazing, exciting or terrible together. You can be almost certain that their memory of the occasion isn't quite the same as yours, even though you experienced exactly the same thing. Sometimes we even create 'false memories' based on stories we know about ourselves that we don't remember. But because we have heard them so many times, as we imagine them, we turn them into memories.

Also, when we talk about what we remember to different people, the way we tell the story may change – and when we do that, the memory changes, too. This is known as the 'audience-tuning' effect. The way you tell a story to someone becomes your memory of what happened, whether or not it is accurate. Our memories change over time depending on our reasons for re-telling them and how we re-tell them. Even as we go over a memory in our heads, we are likely to make small changes to it. And if we can't bring to mind some of the smaller details, we will fill in the gaps over time. What's more, we tend not to question our memories once they are made. So, whatever was our most recent version of the memory becomes the memory itself.

So, next time someone asks whether you're telling the truth and you think you are – you actually may not be!

Lesson 1C

HOW TO ... | express personal preferences
VOCABULARY | emotions and feelings
PRONUNCIATION | word stress: dependent prepositions

VOCABULARY

emotions and feelings

1 A Complete the sentences with *about, by, into, of* or *on*.

1 I'm really passionate .... travel – I love visiting new cities!
2 Melania sounds fed up .... everything today – let's go and cheer her up.
3 I'm terrified .... flying even though I know it's the safest form of transport.
4 Katya was thrilled .... the present you gave her for her birthday.
5 I'm not keen .... going to museums. I just find them really boring.
6 She's really .... Japanese culture. We're hoping to go to Tokyo next year.
7 I'm quite fond .... my auntie – she's such a great listener.
8 I think she's feeling a bit nervous .... the journey.

B Choose the correct phrases to complete the diary.

Day 1

I'm absolutely ¹**passionate about / fond of / fed up of** Spanish food, so I've booked myself onto a cooking course here in Madrid. I felt a little bit ²**not keen on / thrilled by / nervous about** talking to people in Spanish because I haven't done it for ages, but it went well.

Day 2

We made paella today – a famous Spanish rice dish. I'm not that ³**terrified of / nervous about / keen on** rice, but this dish is delicious! Tomorrow we're learning some knife skills. To be honest, I'm really ⁴**terrified of / thrilled about / passionate about** cutting myself – I tend to have a lot of accidents and I'm getting a bit ⁵**keen on / fond of / fed up of** being so clumsy.

Day 3

Phew! Everything went well and we learned about the various ingredients to use in tapas – small snacks. I'm ⁶**fed up of / really into / not keen on** them because there's such a lot of variety and they're so tasty. Flying home tomorrow!

How to ...

express personal preferences

2 A 🔊 1.05 | Listen to a conversation between three friends. What are the speakers talking about? Do they reach a compromise?

B 🔊 1.05 | Listen again and complete the extracts with the missing words.

1 Backpacking's not really ....
2 Sorry, it's just that I'm .... camping.
3 .... go to lots of different places, but stay in some decent hotels?
4 Well, ... go to Thailand.
5 I'd be happy to do a bit of sunbathing, but I .... do it all day.
6 How about travelling around Europe instead? Does that .... ?

PRONUNCIATION

3 A | word stress: dependent prepositions | Read the sentences. Underline the stress in the phrases in bold.

1 I'm quite **fond of** boat trips, actually. They're a great way to see the city.
2 The kids aren't **keen on** trying unusual foods.
3 Dan's **terrified of** driving in foreign countries and so am I!
4 I'm not **really into** visiting museums. I find a lot of them really boring.
5 I always feel **nervous about** getting lost when I'm in a new city.
6 Katie's quite **passionate about** culture and the arts.

B 🔊 1.06 | Now listen and check.

SPEAKING

4 A 🔊 1.07 | Complete the personal introduction with the phrases (a–f). Then listen and check.

> Hi, I'm Jack. I'm ¹............... learning languages and ²............... them for a few years now. ³............... languages is that they give you lots of insight into new cultures. ⁴............... people shouting loudly at waiters in English when they're in another country. ⁵............... give it a go and get it wrong than not try at all. I'm ⁶............... when it comes to learning languages and I can speak three pretty fluently now!

a quite ambitious
b I'd rather
c I've been studying
d The thing I love about
e passionate about
f I can't stand hearing

B Talk about your own hobbies and interests. Use the model in Ex 4A. Record your answer if you can.

Speak anywhere Go to the interactive speaking practice

Lesson 1D

GRAMMAR | *while, whereas* and *whilst*
LISTENING | personality traits

GRAMMAR

while, whereas and whilst

1 A Match the sentence beginnings (1–6) with the endings (a–f).

1 I've always been pretty shy,
2 Whilst I love musicals,
3 I cleaned the bathroom,
4 My brother loves going out,
5 I read an entire book
6 Whilst I'm usually pretty organised,

a my partner absolutely hates them!
b while I was waiting for my connecting flight.
c I was a bit of a mess that day.
d whereas my twin sister is very outgoing.
e whereas I'm more of a stay-at-home type.
f whilst my flatmate made dinner.

B Complete each sentence with one phrase from box A and one phrase from box B.

A

confident with friends   meeting new people
mowed the lawn   my parents   self-esteem
to see you

B

cleaned the house   intimidated by people at work
not very sociable   too much work to do
very confident   walking home

1 Whilst I'm ...., I feel ....
2 Whilst I'd love ...., I've got ....
3 I love ...., whereas Tom is ....
4 I called .... whilst I was ....
5 Whilst Tom ...., I ....
6 Dad lacks ...., whilst mum is ....

LISTENING

2 A 🔊 **1.08** | Listen to the lecture and match the personality traits (1–5) with their definitions (a–e).

1 openness
2 conscientiousness
3 extroversion
4 agreeableness
5 neuroticism

a how helpful and understanding you are towards others
b how energetic, sociable and confident you are
c how responsible and reliable you are
d how likely you are to feel emotions like sadness and anxiety
e how happy you are to try new things and hear new ideas

B 🔊 **1.08** | Listen again and complete each sentence with one or two words.

1 The lecturer says that a .... of the five main personality traits does not exist.
2 A conscientious person is ...., keeps their promises and admits their mistakes.
3 In an ...., a conscientious person will do all their work and turn up on time.
4 The lecturer says that it's unlikely an extrovert will be described as a .... person.
5 If you can understand the .... of other people, you are an agreeable person.
6 The lecturer says that neurotic people tend to have a higher number of ....

C 🔊 **1.09** | Listen to the final sentence again and write what you hear. You will hear the sentence only once.

....
....

Lesson 2A

GRAMMAR | future probability
VOCABULARY | science and technology; word families
PRONUNCIATION | connected speech: future probability

VOCABULARY

science and technology

1 Complete the sentences with the words in the box.

> analyse findings predicted remotely
> researchers smart tech industry virtual reality

1 .... technology didn't exist when my parents were younger – they couldn't even access the internet on their phones!
2 Could you help me .... the results of the experiment? It'll take me ages to review them on my own.
3 In my role, I can work ...., so I don't need to go into the office every day.
4 As ...., the tests were highly successful.
5 Don't forget to include the .... of the study in your report.
6 .... have discovered that VR can provide many of the same benefits as real-world experiences.
7 My mum works in the .... as a software engineer. I hope to follow in her footsteps.
8 I've been practising golf using .... It's almost as good as being on the course.

word families

2 Choose the correct word to complete the sentences.

1 The outcome of the board meeting was entirely .... I knew I'd be forced to resign.
  a remote   **b** predictable   **c** scientific
2 Have you completed the chemical .... yet? We'll need the results of it fairly soon.
  a analysis   **b** science   **c** prediction
3 I'm planning to do some .... into VR in my postgraduate degree.
  a analysis   **b** predictions   **c** research
4 If you want to be a data scientist, you need a highly .... mind.
  a analytical   **b** virtual   **c** predictable
5 There is absolutely no .... evidence to back up your claim.
  a remote   **b** virtual   **c** scientific
6 It's incredible that vehicles on the Moon can be controlled ...., don't you think?
  a scientifically   **b** remotely   **c** virtually

GRAMMAR

future probability

3 A Choose the correct word or phrase to complete the sentences.

1 Paulo says he **definitely won't / will definitely / won't definitely** stop trying to get into his first-choice university.
2 Lisa thinks it's **likely / certain / unlikely** she'll win the photography competition because there were so many great entries.
3 It's **won't / certain to / due to** rain the minute I get out of the car because I haven't brought my umbrella!
4 Hurry up! Bryony's train is **won't / likely to / due to** arrive any minute now.
5 Pasha says he **may not / definitely will / won't** be able to come tonight, but he'll do his best.
6 They said I **could / will / might** work remotely, but I didn't want to. I prefer going into the office.

B Complete the second sentence so that it means the same as the first, using the correct form of the words in brackets.

1 I don't think this experiment is going to work.
  This experiment .... (likely) work.
2 Paula says she's about to start a new project involving VR.
  Paula says she .... (going) start a new a project involving VR.
3 I don't think attending a gig virtually is something I'll ever do – I'd rather be there in person.
  I don't think .... (ever) a gig virtually – I'd much rather be there in person.
4 I'm sure VR will be used in school classrooms eventually.
  VR .... (certain) be used in school classrooms eventually.
5 You're handing in your report today, aren't you?
  You're .... (due) your report today, aren't you?
6 I've thought about finding a job in the tech industry, but I haven't decided yet.
  I .... (might) a job in the tech industry, but I haven't decided yet.

PRONUNCIATION

4 A 🔊 **2.01** | connected speech: future probability | Listen and complete the sentences.

1 VR is .... come down in price eventually.
2 Robert's .... start his new job on Monday.
3 Are you .... bring your headset with you?
4 You're .... catch anything out in the open.
5 Joseph .... study law at university.
6 VR is .... be in every household by 2030.

B 🔊 **2.01** | Listen again and repeat.

READING

5 A Read the article and choose the main topic (a or b) of each paragraph (1–6).

Paragraph 1
a checking how experiments have gone
b making necessary changes to experiments

Paragraph 2
a ensuring things are being done properly
b carrying out daily tasks and duties

Paragraph 3
a discussing work with seniors
b writing up

Paragraph 4
a motivating other people
b teaching in a lab

Paragraph 5
a gaining inspiration for work
b chatting to others in the field

Paragraph 6
a offering students useful advice
b providing assistance to students

B Read the article again. Are the statements True (T) or False (F)?

1 Students are given regular support on the experiments they're doing.
2 Daniela refuses to do certain tasks outside of the lab.
3 Daniela does not especially enjoy one important part of her job.
4 Daniela says she is sometimes jealous of her students' ability to come up with ideas.
5 Daniela usually finds her conference talks go well.
6 Daniela thinks students should not work too hard in the lab.

A day in the life …
research scientist Dr Daniela Brown

8.45 a.m.
[1]Based at a university, I supervise research students as they carry out experiments in the lab. It's my role to keep them – the students *and* the experiments! – on track, so the first thing I do when I arrive is to take a look at the results of any experiments that were running overnight. If an experiment didn't go as predicted, I might adapt it and get the students to repeat it in a slightly different way.

9.30–10.30 a.m.
[2]After this, I head to my office to go through my emails. That can take some time! I could do it remotely, but when I go home in the evening, I prefer to switch off. My job can be pretty stressful and I think it's important to have some down-time. While I'm in my office, I might also do a bit of reading. I'll maybe look through scientific journals or reference books. I also like to make sure I'm doing all the technical stuff for the experiments right, so I'll double-check on techniques and report back to the students if need be.

10.35 a.m.–1.00 p.m.
[3]Then I'll grab a coffee and settle down to analyse the results of previous days' experiments, and I might spend some time reporting on my findings, too. Getting papers published for others to read is an essential part of any research job, though I prefer practical work, so writing up can seem a bit like hard work! Thankfully, I have my own supervisor who I can approach with any questions or ask for help if I get stuck. It's important for any researcher to be able to discuss ideas with other experts.

13.45–4.30 p.m.
[4]After lunch, I'll spend some time in the lab with the students. They will have questions of their own, though I can't always answer them! In science, there's always trial and error, but I encourage them to find solutions and new ways of doing things. I don't pretend to know it all because I certainly don't. What always amazes me is that someone will always come up with a way of doing something that I've never even thought about.

9.00 a.m.–5.00 p.m. (on occasion)
[5]Occasionally, my day will involve attending a scientific conference instead. I haven't presented at one yet, but it's fascinating to see what else is going on out there in the scientific community, and it often informs what I might decide to work on next.

6.00 p.m.
[6]Before my working day ends, I will go back to the lab after a bit more time in my office to see how the research students have got on during the day and to answer their questions. I'll also help out with setting up any experiments that will run overnight. I'll remind students not to work too late and to get some much-needed rest before I log off and head out of the lab myself.

Lesson 2B

GRAMMAR | quantifiers
VOCABULARY | nature
PRONUNCIATION | connected speech: quantifiers

VOCABULARY

nature

1 A Match the sentence beginnings (1–6) with the endings (a–f) to make sentences.

1 Look at the way the sunlight is
2 I love deserted beaches like this –
3 The coastline stretches for 3,000 km
4 This entire area is
5 You can cycle down this track
6 I just sat on the river bank,

a from one end of the country to another.
b creating a beautiful pattern on the ground.
c known for its amazing scenery.
d watching the boats go by.
e all the way into the city.
f no one around for miles and miles.

B Complete the text with nature words or phrases.

WILLOWS WELL-BEING RETREAT

Location

Surrounded by ¹_____ the only thing interrupting the peace at the Willows Well-being Retreat is the sound of birdsong and leaves moving on the trees. Or if you find yourself standing on the ²_____, the gentle sound of water rushing by.

Facilities

- World-class dining
- Freshwater swimming pool
- Large ³_____ amongst the trees for yoga classes.

Activities

From forest bathing to hiking along ancient ⁴_____ through the landscape, there is a wide variety of well-being activities to choose from during your stay. For those who prefer being less active, simply sit and enjoy the beautiful ⁵_____ around you or bathe in the ⁶_____ shining warmly through the trees.

We look forward to welcoming you at Willows!

GRAMMAR

quantifiers

2 A Choose the correct word or phrase to complete the sentences.

1 I suspect there are **few / a little / a few** rooftop gardens in this area because the houses don't have flat roofs.
2 **No / None / Not any** wildflowers should be taken from these woods as it will have a negative effect on the ecosystem.
3 Only a **little / majority / minority** of residents are in favour of the plans to change the shared lawn into a vegetable plot.
4 There's **a minority / a little / little** countryside left in the region – it's almost all been built on.
5 I found **a handful of / a lack of / plenty of** new cycling routes round here – not many, but it might be interesting to see where they go.
6 I know **a little / a few / few** people who really enjoy gardening, but it's not really my thing.

B Read the sentences and correct the quantifiers in bold.

1 There are only a **little** of vegan restaurants in the city where I live.
2 **Few** of my friends live in the countryside, but most live in urban areas.
3 **No** time I go to the beach I come back feeling refreshed and relaxed. It's awesome.
4 There are **a handful of** parks in my town at all, so we have to play football at the sports centre.
5 There's a definite **little** of green spaces in my local neighbourhood.
6 I see very **a little** wildlife in my garden because I live in the city.
7 I spend a good **majority** of time walking in the forest near my house.
8 There are **no** open spaces in my city, but the ones we do have are pleasant.

PRONUNCIATION

3 A 🔊 **2.02** | connected speech: quantifiers | Draw a line ⌒ between any words that link together in the phrases in bold. Then listen and check.

1 There's **a lack of** attractive green spaces in my town.
2 Only **a handful of** people I know live in the countryside.
3 I spend **a good deal of** time outdoors.
4 **Several of the** beaches nearby are quite good.
5 Young people who like gardening **are in a minority**.

B 🔊 **2.02** | Listen and repeat.

LISTENING

4 A 🔊 **2.03** | Listen to the introduction to a radio programme. Choose the correct topic (a–c).

  a The benefits of gardening as we get older
  b How people of all ages enjoy gardening together
  c Young people who enjoy gardening

B 🔊 **2.04** | Listen to the next part of the radio programme and answer the questions.

Which speaker … ?

  a says how pleased they are that they have learned about plants? ....
  b became interested in gardening because of a local scheme? ....
  c noticed a difference in their mood after doing some gardening? ....
  d Is excited about something that is going to happen soon? ....
  e became suddenly more aware of their surroundings? ....
  f mentions one reason that gardening may have a particular benefit? ....

C 🔊 **2.04** | Listen again. Are the statements True (T) or False (F)?

  1 Speaker 1 started gardening because she wanted to test a theory.
  2 Speaker 1 is confident about why she had benefitted from time in the garden.
  3 Speaker 2 likes getting away from her living accommodation for a while.
  4 Speaker 2 quickly came to realise that gardening could be interesting.
  5 Speaker 2 understands that different tasks should be done at different times of year.
  6 Speaker 3 did not use to know exactly why seaside landscapes were so beautiful.
  7 Speaker 3 has little idea of what she is really doing with the plants on her balcony.

D 🔊 **2.05** | Listen to the final speaker again and write what you hear. You will hear the sentence only once.

....

WRITING

a for-and-against essay

5 A Read the article and choose the main topic (a–c).

  a The benefits of walking in the rain.
  b Why people dislike walking in the rain.
  c How to enjoy walking in the rain.

B Complete the article with *although*, *despite*, *however* or *while*.

Wet weather walking

Cary Stuart | Thurs 12 Aug | 10.12 GMT

¹.................. the fact that we're repeatedly told to spend more time in nature, few of us actually do. ².................. it's true that it's often raining and cold in the UK, there are ways to making walking in wet weather more appealing.

You may have heard the expression, 'There's no such thing as bad weather – only bad clothing'. ³.................. it's easy enough to buy wet weather gear, it means making a bit more effort to get out of the house. ⁴.................., if you take that extra step, you might just find it was worth it.

To avoid getting really wet on your walk, try taking a route through woodland, where the trees provide cover. ⁵.................., remember that rain can still drip through the branches, so don't take off your raincoat just yet!

The best way to enjoy a walk in the rain is to set off with the right attitude. Then, ⁶.................. the fact you're getting a little wet, you can really start to appreciate nature in all weathers.

C Correct the mistakes in the sentences.

  1 Despite I love living in the city, I also like getting out into the countryside from time to time.
  2 My apartment has got a fantastic view. Although, I'm starting to find it a little small.
  3 Despite many people I know prefer renting, I've decided to save up and buy a house.
  4 However there can be a great sense of community in villages, everyone knows your business, too!
  5 Although the fact that public transport is so good in the city, many people still insist on driving.
  6 I think there are very few downsides to living in the country. Despite, I'll admit it can be boring at times.

D You are going to write a for-and-against essay about whether spending time indoors or outdoors is better for our well-being. Make notes in each column.

for	against

E Write your essay using your notes to help you. Write 100–140 words.

Lesson 2C

HOW TO ... | speculate
VOCABULARY | lifestyle adjectives
PRONUNCIATION | stress to show certainty

VOCABULARY

lifestyle adjectives

1 Choose the correct word to complete the magazine article.

An interview with ...
a storm chaser

In this week's 'Interview with a ...', Zen Magazine talked to Micky Nguyen, who has the fascinating-sounding job of storm chaser.

Zen Magazine (ZM): Being a storm chaser sounds like a pretty ¹**harsh / unique** job! I've never even heard of it.

Micky Nguyen (MN): You're right! The work is far from ²**ordinary / modest**, and I never expected to do this for a living. More and more people are starting to do it, though.

ZM: So, tell us what it involves. Following storms around ... ?

MN: Yeah, I have to get up close to storms so that I can place sensors to record weather data. The conditions can be ³**rewarding / harsh**, particularly in winter when most storms occur.

ZM: Why is there a need for what you do?

MN: It helps weather forecasters be able to give better storm warnings. It's ⁴**tedious / rewarding** in that way because I know I'm helping people.

ZM: You drive all over the country – isn't that ⁵**unique / exhausting**?

MN: I do get tired, yes. And there are risks. I could get struck by lightning! I never have, though. That sense of danger is exciting but I'm very careful.

ZM: Well, it certainly doesn't sound boring!

MN: Never! I used to work in an office and the work was pretty ⁶**tedious / rewarding**. The days would stretch on forever. The salary was better – I'm on quite ⁷**unique / modest** pay now in comparison, but I wouldn't change a thing!

How to ...

speculate

2 A 🔊 2.06 | Listen to three conversations between friends. What do they speculate about?

B 🔊 2.06 | Match the sentence beginnings (1–8) with the endings (a–h). Then listen again and check.

1 I suppose it depends
2 I'd have thought it
3 I reckon you could
4 I bet we'll settle in
5 I know for a fact that
6 There's no way I'll
7 I doubt there'll be
8 I'd imagine the

a easily get cut off though.
b forget home so easily!
c on how remote it is.
d farmers will stay …
e in no time!
f anyone here in 100 years' time!
g we're going to meet …
h wouldn't feel so small.

PRONUNCIATION

3 🔊 2.07 | **stress to show certainty** | Listen and underline the stressed word in each sentence.

1 There's no way I'd ever consider travelling solo round the world.
2 I know for a fact that I'd feel like I was in prison on a tiny boat.
3 He's obviously not happy where he is at the moment.
4 You're clearly not someone who wants a conventional lifestyle.
5 Tom's bound to live a life of adventure – he can't keep still!

SPEAKING

4 A 🔊 2.08 | Complete the conversation with one word in each gap. Then listen and check.

Oli: I'd ¹_____ Kwame's feeling nervous about the play tomorrow.

Cara: It's the first night, right? I get the ²_____ he's feeling pretty confident, actually.

Oli: Oh, yeah?

Cara: Yes – I know for a ³_____ that he's learned his lines off by heart.

Oli: Well, I'd guess you have to, really. There's no ⁴_____ I could be an actor.

Cara: Why not? I'm 100% ⁵_____ that you'd be brilliant at it!

Oli: No, I'd be ⁶_____ to get stage fright!

B 🔊 2.09 | You are Cara in the conversation in Ex 4A. Listen and speak after the beep. Record the conversation if you can.

C Listen to your recording and compare it to Ex 4A.

Speak-anywhere Go to the interactive speaking practice

Lesson 2D

VOCABULARY | extreme adjectives
READING | time travel

VOCABULARY

extreme adjectives

1 Choose the correct word to complete the sentences.
1 Paris during the 1920s was home to the **astonishing / incredible / finest** writers and artists of the age.
2 Have you ever seen a van Gogh painting in real life? They're **magnificent / mighty / precious**.
3 The **finest / mighty / precious** Amazon River winds its way through the rainforest.
4 The museum contains valuable pieces of jewellery which contain **precious / finest / mighty** stones.
5 Only the **magnificent / incredible / finest** coffee beans are used in this unique blend.
6 I can't believe how fast you can run – it's **astonishing / mighty / precious**!

READING

2 A Skim the article quickly and answer the questions.

Do scientists think it is possible to:
1 travel forwards in time?
2 travel backwards in time?

B Complete the sentences with words from the article. Write between one and three words.
1 The writer says that we do not find our own kind of time travel ....
2 The writer suggests that un-doing .... would be a good reason to travel back in time.
3 The writer refers to a theory known as .... , which involves complex mathematics.
4 If we lived on the ISS for a long time, we wouldn't need to apply ....
5 Einstein's .... tell us that backwards time travel is theoretically possible.
6 Unfortunately, the .... make travelling back in time impossible in reality.
7 Scientists are aware of .... , although it is impossible to see it.
8 Tunnels, known as .... , could allow us to travel enormous distances.

C Read the article again. What would make a good concluding sentence?
a It looks as though time travel to the future is more likely than to the past!
b For the moment, maths can only suggest that time travel is possible – but watch this 'space'!
c You never know, time travel could be a reality in the *very* near future!

Is time travel actually possible?

Sofia Valdez | 20th Oct | 12.02 GMT

You may have seen *Doctor Who*, *Back to the Future* or read *The Time Traveller's Wife*, but can you imagine yourself jumping into the future or back into the past? Is it even a possibility? Here's what the scientists say.

We all travel through time, second by second, minute by minute, hour by hour. But there doesn't seem to be anything incredible about that (unless you stop and think about it) because it's our norm, and, much as we might like to go backwards in time, perhaps to correct our mistakes or experience something fantastic again, we can only go forwards. Scientists say we can travel faster if we want to. But explaining *that* involves Einstein and theories and physics and maths, and something known as 'space-time'. (It's all a bit complicated.)

Astronauts are the nearest we have to *actual* time travellers. They can be in space for several weeks or months. When they're on the International Space Station (ISS), they're moving faster than the rest of us back on Earth. This actually creates a situation where they're going slower in time than we are on Earth. (It's true, trust us.) If they were there for years, they'd age better than the rest of us. So, perhaps space travel is better than face creams and anti-aging diets!

But can we go *back* in time? Unfortunately, Earth's physics simply don't allow it. But if we return to Einstein for a minute, we know that some of his mathematical calculations do indeed suggest travelling back in time is possible. The problem is that although Einstein might have *theoretically* proven we can go back in time, in fact, all the other laws of physics really do make it impossible.

This doesn't stop scientists from trying, though! We know that dark matter exists (parts of the universe that we can't see because they don't give off energy or light – as far as we know). And in that dark matter, there *might* be 'wormholes' (theoretical tunnels through space and time). If there are, we could travel from one area of space to another – which could be billions of kilometres away *and* in a different place in time.

1–2 REVIEW

GRAMMAR

1 Choose the correct words to complete the sentences.
1. How long have you **learned** / **been learning** Japanese?
2. I've **emailed** / **been emailing** her three times today.
3. How many times have you **been** / **been going** to India?
4. Have you **had** / **been having** your hair cut? It's looks great!
5. I'm so tired because I've **worked** / **been working** a lot today, and I still haven't finished.

2 Complete the email with the correct form of the verbs in brackets.

Hey Alex!

How's life? Things are pretty much the same here, although I had a pretty terrible day yesterday! I tried ¹_____ (repair) the washing machine myself – bad idea! It flooded the kitchen. I wanted ²_____ (save) money by doing it myself but in the end, it cost me a fortune. Because I was messing about so long with that, I forgot ³_____ (go) to my dentist's appointment for the third time, so they've taken me off their system. Then I stopped ⁴_____ (get) some shopping on my way back from the gym – I got to the till and realised I didn't have my bank card with me. It was a nightmare!

What else? Oh, I know. Do you remember ⁵_____ (go) to that festival where we met Andi and Niamh? I bumped into them the other week. I was in the park and they stopped ⁶_____ (say) hello. They asked how you were.

The only other thing to report is that I'm thinking of looking for a new job. My idea is ⁷_____ (retrain) as a physiotherapist. I just want ⁸_____ (do) something more worthwhile with my life.

Anyway, I'm looking forward to ⁹_____ (see) you in September for our holiday!

Speak again soon,

Chris

3 Use the prompts to write sentences using *while*, *whilst* or *whereas*.
1. enjoy writing stories ✓
   a brilliant imagination ✗
2. actually quite shy ✓
   love performing on stage ✓
3. can organise other people ✓
   organise myself ✗
4. happy to listen to people's problems ✓
   like giving advice ✗
5. enjoy playing football ✗ (never)
   enjoy watching it ✓ (always)

4 Complete the article with the correct future form of the words in brackets.

What next?

If you're due ¹_____ (leave) university soon and feel a little overwhelmed about what's ²_____ (happen), don't worry! With a little planning, it ³_____ (might not be) quite as scary as it sounds.

If you know you definitely ⁴_____ (not enjoy) a graduate job in a big firm, there are other options. You ⁵_____ (be able) to apply for a postgraduate course as soon as you graduate, and you ⁶_____ (also be) in a good place to start your own business. You certainly ⁷_____ (not need) a ton of money if you're offering a service such as web design or social media influencing. But you may ⁸_____ (able) to apply for a bank loan if you want to start, say, an online shop.

Another possibility is to take a gap year to consider your future. While you're travelling, you're likely ⁹_____ (meet) new people and discover more about the world, which ¹⁰_____ (give) you new ideas about your future.

5 Choose the correct word or phrase to complete the sentences.
1. Only **a few** / **a little** / **a lack of** cheese on my spaghetti, please!
2. The **minority of** / **lack of** / **majority of** affordable housing in this country is a real issue.
3. There **are some** / **aren't any** / **are little** places left for the Escape Room event, I'm afraid.
4. The **majority** / **minority** / **plenty** of people who live here have family in the area.
5. **Very few** / **Plenty of** / **Quite a few** people know the secret ingredient – just me and my father.

VOCABULARY

6 Match the personality adjectives in the box with the descriptions (1–5).

| adventurous   argumentative |
| curious   rebellious   stubborn |

1. He was an awful teenager. He refused to do what he was told and caused trouble instead.
2. It doesn't matter what we're talking about, my brother always seems to disagree.
3. My daughter just loves finding out new things. She's always asking questions.
4. She's already climbed Mount Everest. Apparently, she's now planning to trek through the Amazon!
5. It doesn't matter what you tell him – he won't change his mind.

REVIEW 1–2

7 Complete the sentences with the adjective form of the words in brackets.
1 Sofia's quite an .... (experience) skater now and is entering her first major championship.
2 I'm pretty .... (optimist) about the future of the planet – we're making great progress.
3 Tonya isn't a .... (rely) employee and often turns up late or not at all.
4 I'm feeling quite .... (emotion) after seeing my daughter graduate.
5 I've never been very .... (practice). I can't even change a lightbulb!

8 Complete the text with the words in the box.

| brought   by heart   childhood   detail |
| memory   recall   short-term |

We have near-perfect ¹............ when it comes to dangerous or threatening things that have happened to us, but it's impossible for us to remember every ²............. Over time, we forget things, regardless of the fact we like to think we have a good ³.............
While our ⁴............ memory might work pretty well soon after acquiring new information, if we don't make the effort to learn things ⁵............, we won't remember them for long at all, especially if they aren't important for our survival.

9 Choose the correct words to complete the sentences.
1 Oh, that name **slipped my mind / rings a bell**! Is she the one that used to work on reception?
2 I can never remember things like dates. They just **go in one ear and out the other / refresh my memory**.
3 Didn't I leave the keys on the table? My memory is **ringing a bell / playing tricks on me**.
4 No, don't tell me. Hold on, it's **gone in one ear and out the other / on the tip of my tongue**!
5 I know you've told me the story before but go on, **refresh my memory / slip my mind**.

10 Complete the phrasal verbs in the sentences with *about, by, into, of, on* or *up*.
1 I'm really fed .... of living in this town – it's so boring. Nothing ever happens!
2 I'm quite fond .... going to the cinema on Mondays, when it's quiet.
3 My brother's really .... futsal. It's like football, but with a smaller ball.
4 So, what are you passionate ....? Personally, I love music and fashion.
5 Mum's not keen .... soup – let's make pasta for lunch instead.

11 Choose the correct word or phrase to complete the sentences.
1 Further .... seems to confirm that VR can have a positive impact on recall.
  a analysis   b researchers   c findings
2 According to recent data, only twenty percent of people in the .... industry are women.
  a smart   b remote   c tech
3 As ...., participants that played video games demonstrated better social skills.
  a findings   b predicted   c analysis
4 .... working on the project have said they expect to have results by the end of the year.
  a Researchers   b Findings   c Tech industry
5 The company has said these .... will revolutionise the field of VR.
  a analysis   b tech   c findings

12 Complete the conversation with the correct form of the words in brackets.
A: How's the ¹............ (research) going?
B: Well, as ²............ (predict), it's taking a long time. But I've done all the ³............ (analyse) of the experiments, so I'll meet the deadline.
A: Good for you! Do you think you'll become a full-time ⁴............ (research) after this?
B: I'm not sure. I definitely want to do some kind of ⁵............ (science) work related to my studies, though. How's your job?
A: OK. I've been offered the opportunity to work ⁶............ (remote) and just go into the office once a week, which would really suit me.

13 Complete the sentences with the words in the box.

| deserted   river bank   scenery   sunlight   woodland |

1 The .... is so bright, it's hurting my eyes!
2 Fishing is so boring. You just sit on the .... all day, not talking.
3 Urgh! I'm sick of work. I wish I were on a .... beach somewhere, lying in the sun.
4 This area of .... is made up of hundreds of different types of trees.
5 The .... around here is amazing. I could look at it for hours.

14 Choose the correct words to complete the sentences.
1 This TV series is really **tedious / rewarding**. I don't think I'll finish it.
2 I think you're **ordinary / unique** – there's no one else like you!
3 I'm quite **modest / harsh**. I don't like to make my achievements seem better than they are.
4 I'm going to tell you the truth. It might sound **harsh / exhausting**, but at least it will be honest.
5 It's really **rewarding / ordinary** when I put the effort in, and achieve something at the end.

15 Choose the correct meanings for the adjectives.
1 The royal palace is truly **magnificent**.
  a very impressive   b very expensive
2 It's **astonishing** how successful the blog has been.
  a very exciting   b very surprising
3 Mm, this is the **finest** cheese I've ever tasted!
  a the best   b the softest
4 I love your baby! She must be so **precious** to you.
  a very important   b very expensive
5 What an **incredible** view! You're lucky to live here.
  a completely impossible   b extremely great

17

Lesson 3A

GRAMMAR | relative clauses
VOCABULARY | festivals; the environment
PRONUNCIATION | pitch in non-defining relative clauses

VOCABULARY

festivals

1 Complete the blog post with the correct form of the words in the box.

> act atmosphere attend attract
> festival-goer line-up organiser venue

SherryG
Mon 30 Jul | 09.33

Just back from ¹_____ WOMAD festival and it was awesome! There was a fantastic ²_____ of artists from all over the world – not just music but dance and other arts, too. I saw as many ³_____ as I could during the four days I was there and none of them disappointed. The ⁴_____ was amazing – everyone was singing, dancing and having a great time.

The festival grounds are huge, and all of the ⁵_____ certainly did a good job of making it easy to get around the enormous ⁶_____, which stretched over several large fields. It's a beautiful place, too – no wonder the festival ⁷_____ such a massive number of people. I think there were about 40,000 ⁸_____ in total! You should definitely go!

the environment

2 Choose the correct word to complete the sentences.
1 Driving less is the simplest way for individuals to reduce their carbon **footprint / power / emission**.
2 We need to move away from natural **emissions / power / resources** such as oil and gas and look for sustainable alternatives.
3 We've introduced a **recycling / renewable / clean-up** scheme at work for cardboard, glass and metal.
4 Carbon **emissions / power / footprints** will drop by forty percent if the current targets are met.
5 More and more organisations are turning to **clean-up / renewable / recycling** energy such as wind and solar power.
6 We can't depend on solar **resources / emissions / power** in our country because the weather's so bad!

GRAMMAR

relative clauses

3 A The sentences below have a mistake. Choose the best option to correct the mistake.
1 Everyone <u>in which</u> we've spoken to has really enjoyed the event.
   a what   b which   c who
2 My mum, <u>that is</u> a singer-songwriter, is appearing at the Edinburgh Festival this year.
   a who's   b which   c whose
3 That's the album <u>which is</u> they're most famous for.
   a when   b what   c that
4 Camp Bestival, <u>who</u> attracts thousands of visitors every year, takes place in the UK.
   a where   b which   c that

B Read the sentences in Ex 3A again. In which can you omit the relative pronoun?

PRONUNCIATION

4 A 🔊 3.01 | pitch in non-defining relative clauses | Listen and underline the clauses with a lower pitch.
1 Glastonbury Festival, which has been running since 1970, attracts over 200,000 visitors.
2 The band, who had never played to such a large crowd before, felt very nervous.
3 The headline act, which will perform this evening, is expected to draw a huge crowd.
4 Billie Eilish, who has sold over 5 million records worldwide, will be on stage at nine.
5 The orchestra, which is bigger than ever, will play on the Sticks stage this afternoon.
6 Woodstock, which took place over three days in 1969, was a turning point in music.

B 🔊 3.01 | Listen again and repeat.

READING

5 A Read the article and tick the topics that are mentioned.

eco-businesses   food waste   green festivals
product quality   renewable energy
sustainable products   transport   water usage

Be a greener festival-goer!

Here are our top tips to help you cut your festival carbon footprint …

Tip 1: Go to environmentally-friendly festivals
Start off in the right way by choosing to attend a green festival, whose organisers will make cleaner decisions on your behalf, including powering their grounds with green energy, providing recycling bins, and committing to environmental policies.

Tip 2: Stay local
Instead of travelling long distances to go a festival, choose one that is closer to home. Bands often do the festival circuit around the country, so you'll still get to see your favourite performers. You'll also have the opportunity to see up-and-coming bands in your area and add some new favourites.

Tip 3: Re-think your 'stuff'
It's easy to pack your rucksack full of mini-bottles of shampoo, shower gel and hair products, but too many of these still come in unnecessary plastic packaging. Fortunately, there are alternatives: you can take – or make – shampoo bars, bamboo toothbrushes, and natural deodorants; and some companies have refill stations, where you can take along a reusable container and fill up with your favourite toiletries before the festival.

Tip 4: Buy once, buy well
Many festival-goers actually leave their tents behind after the event, not realising the majority end up in landfill. So, instead of purchasing a single-use festival tent, invest in something high-quality and reusable. It'll be more comfortable, too. And go plastic-free by taking along reusable water bottles and coffee cups.

Tip 5: Be an electricity saver
Festivals usually have charging points for mobile phones but these come at a cost. Why not take your own pocket charger? All you have to do is wind it up and it'll provide charge for your phone. And why not decorate your tent with solar-powered fairy lights to make it stand out from the crowd – and help you find your way home at night!

B Read the text and answer the questions. Use no more than three words for each answer.

1 What are many green festivals committing to?
....
2 To fill up your reusable containers, where should you take them to?
....
3 What can you do if you use reusable water bottles and coffee cups?
....
4 What do you need to do to use a pocket charger?
....

WRITING

a formal email

6 A Read the email from a local resident to the organisers of a festival. What is the purpose of the email?

¹Hi,

I live in the countryside where XFest is held annually. Every year, I ²get more and more fed up with the mess left behind by festival-goers, who ³couldn't care less about the damage they are causing to the local environment.

I have been involved in clean-up operations for the last few years and ⁴hate the amount of waste that is left in the fields. I know that some of the camping gear is rescued and given to homeless charities, but this doesn't ⁵sort out the problem of it being buried or the ground being damaged.

Is there no way you can insist on campers leaving the place as they found it?

⁶Can't wait to hear from you all!

Suki Wolensson, Kent

B Read the email again. Replace the underlined informal phrases (1–6) with their more formal equivalents (a–f).
 a become increasingly frustrated by
 b strongly disapprove of
 c address the issue of
 d I look forward to your response.
 e appear to have little concern
 f To whom it may concern,

C Imagine you are one of the organisers of XFest. Plan a formal response to the email in Ex 6A.

D Write your formal email. Write 100–140 words.

7 Read the question. Then plan, write and review your answer. You must write at least 75 words.

Governments should make people look after their local environment. Do you agree or disagree with this statement? Why/Why not?

Lesson 3B

GRAMMAR | cleft sentences
VOCABULARY | phrasal verbs: performing; phrasal verbs: communication
PRONUNCIATION | emphatic stress

VOCABULARY

phrasal verbs: performing

1 A Choose the correct phrase to complete the sentences.

1 The play certainly didn't .... my expectations. It was all pretty disappointing.
   a come up with   **b** live up to   **c** end up
2 Stand-up comedians often have to .... heckling from members of the audience.
   a put up with   **b** end up   **c** carry on
3 I totally .... my lines in our dress rehearsal. Let's hope things go well on opening night.
   a put me off   **b** fell back on   **c** messed up
4 Who .... the name for this show? *Fairy Lights* sounds like a children's programme!
   a lived up to   **b** carried on   **c** came up with
5 I slipped on stage and .... falling into the orchestra pit! It was so embarrassing!
   a ended up   **b** fell back on   **c** carried on

B Complete the forum posts with the phrasal verbs in the box. There are two you don't need.

> came up with   carry on   ended up   fall back on
> live up to   mess up   put up with   put you off

Calling all street performers!

 Felix99   Yesterday at 9.36 p.m.

Hi, all! I'm currently studying music at uni, but I'm struggling to pay the fees this term. I'm a pretty decent musician, so I'm thinking of doing a bit of busking to help me ¹.............. with my studies. And maybe if I fail all of my exams it'll give me something to ² ....! Ha ha! So, what's the job really like? Thanks!

Comments

 Perry   Yesterday at 9.48 p.m.

Hey, Felix. I'm a busker and ³.............. the idea in the same way you did – to get a bit of extra cash. Obviously, it means a lot of performing out in the cold and you can be there for hours! Don't let that ⁴.............., though – it's fun and if you're good enough, you can earn a decent amount. Good luck!

 Kittykat02   Yesterday at 10.01 p.m.

I ⁵.............. busking for a bit last year and it was hard work. You'll have to ⁶.............. a lot of difficult people and you **WILL** get cold and stiff after a while. It's still great fun though.

phrasal verbs: communication

2 Choose the correct words to complete the text messages.

> Hey, Antonio! How did the presentation go?
> 4.32

> Hey! Yeah, not too bad. They kept asking me to ¹**speak up / bring up** though because my mic wasn't working properly.
> 4.35

> Oh, really? But did you still manage to ²**come across your message / get your message across**?
> 4.36

> More or less. I did have to ³**spell out / speak up** the need for us to be better at recycling. Every day I find plastic in the normal bin, loads of waste paper by the photocopier … We've talked about it before so it's a bit frustrating having to keep ⁴**coming back to / pointing out** the same point.
> 4.37

> Yeah, that must be pretty annoying! Did you ⁵**move on / bring up** your idea for the renewable energy programme?
> 4.38

> No, I decided to leave that for now. Anyway, how did your interview go?
> 4.39

> Well, they said I ⁶**spoke up / came across** well, but I didn't get the job. In the feedback, they ⁷**pointed out that / came back to** the candidate who got the job had a lot more experience.
> 4.41

> Oh, no! Sorry, mate. Well, never mind. Take what you can from the experience and ⁸**come back to / move on from** it.

> Thanks, I will!

GRAMMAR

cleft sentences

3 A Match the sentences beginnings (1–6) with the endings (a–f).

1 What theatre performers enjoy
2 It was my school drama teacher, Ms White
3 What I hoped to get across in the screenplay
4 What happened next
5 What Hannah wanted to do as a child
6 What I'd really like to find out
7 It was only when we finished the play
8 What I really love about being in a band

a who suggested I apply to acting school.
b was that Johannes fell off the stage!
c is making music with my friends.
d is getting immediate feedback from the audience.
e that we discovered there was a talent scout in the crowd.
f was become an opera singer.
g is whether I'm playing the lead role.
h was the character's sense of despair.

B The sentences below have a mistake. Choose the best option to correct the mistake.

1 That I want to know is how to get into film acting.
   a It's   b What   c How
2 It was Candice who wants to go into the circus, not Toni.
   a who want   b which wants
   c who wanted
3 It were my grandparents who gave me my 'lucky' socks.
   a was   b is   c are
4 It the performers did was pretend to be audience members.
   a They're   b It's   c What

PRONUNCIATION

4 A 🔊 3.02 | **emphatic stress** | Listen and underline the stressed words.

1 What I like watching are the less well-known acts.
2 It was Max who left the car unlocked, not me.
3 What sounds better to me is finishing on a minor chord.
4 It's you who likes Italian opera – that's why I got the tickets!

B 🔊 3.02 | Listen again and repeat.

LISTENING

5 A 🔊 3.03 | Listen to a conversation between two friends, about a stage performance. Number the pictures in the correct order.

B 🔊 3.03 | Listen again. Are the statements True (T) or False (F)?

1 Alex's partner did not think she had got her lines wrong.
2 Katy worried that she would make mistakes on stage.
3 Katy thinks it may have been her fault that there was a problem with Alex's costume.
4 The crew in charge of the scenery were able to resolve an issue straightaway.
5 All the audience members wanted a refund of their tickets.
6 Katy thinks that people who watch a performance want the actors to do well.

C 🔊 3.04 | Listen and complete the phrases.

1 It was like, a total _____!
2 I'd practised, like, a _____ times!
3 I could hardly stand up, I was _____ so much.
4 … it was like the _____ day of my life!
5 You feel as if you're going to die of _____.
6 I bet your time on stage seemed to go on _____!

D 🔊 3.05 | Listen to the recording and write what you hear. You will hear the sentence only once.

_____

Lesson 3C

HOW TO ... | use vague language
VOCABULARY | film and TV
PRONUNCIATION | linking and elision

VOCABULARY

film and TV

1 A Complete the review with the words in the box. There is one word which you do not need.

> based   cast   costumes   ending   scenes
> set   soundtrack   subtitles   twist

Review of Daniel Craig's last James Bond film, *No Time to Die*
★★★★☆

Many James Bond films are ¹_____ on novels by Ian Fleming, but this one was written specially for the film. The ²_____ includes Daniel Craig as the retired (!) James Bond, along with Ralph Fiennes as M, Ben Wishaw as Q, and Léa Seydoux as Madeleine.

The film is ³_____ in Italy and on a remote island, and the scenery – as always in James Bond films – is stunning. There are the usual action-filled car chase ⁴_____, which are always fun, as well as some more emotional ones, for example, when Bond is with his girlfriend – and her young child. The ⁵_____ is unexpected! I wouldn't call it a ⁶_____ as such, but there are certainly some surprises!

As for the ⁷_____, well, it's the usual James Bond suit and nothing else very exciting. The ⁸_____ is as great as ever, with dramatic music throughout and the well-known James Bond theme, though unfortunately, we never actually hear the full tune!

B Choose the correct word to complete the sentences.

1 I have to put the **soundtrack / costumes / subtitles** on when I watch a film because I can't hear very well.
2 My current favourite series is **cast / set / based** in Sweden – it's a 'Scandi noir' murder mystery.
3 I love a good **twist / ending / set** in a film or novel – it's exciting to find out what happens next.
4 I thought the **cast / scene / set** was brilliant. The main actor doesn't usually play mean characters!
5 I loved the **ending / scene / subtitle** where James meets the new 007. It makes you wonder what's going to happen.
6 It annoys me when they make a film **subtitled / based / set** on a best-selling book and then change the ending!

How to ...

use vague language

2 A 🔊 3.06 | Listen and tick the phrases you hear.

> and stuff   bits   old-ish   sort of
> something like that   that kind of thing

B 🔊 3.07 | Match the questions (1–5) with the vague replies (a–e). Then listen and check.

1 Who's that guy who played the thief in *Lupin*?
2 When was the *Great Gatsby* supposed to be set?
3 How old do you think the actor in *Maid* is?
4 Did you enjoy watching *The Originals*?
5 Is *Money Heist* a dark story?

a I'd say she's young-ish … maybe late 20s?
b It was OK. It's sort of for a younger audience, really.
c It's what's his name – oh, you know!
d I suppose it is, a bit. But I like that kind of thing.
e Around the 1920s, I think.

PRONUNCIATION

3 🔊 3.08 | **linking and elision** | Listen and complete the sentences. Then listen again and repeat.

1 I love _____ in a good mystery series.
2 I like the film. It's _____ a combination of action and thriller.
3 I love dramas that are _____ real events.
4 *The Crystal Maze*? Oh, that's where they run around and find crystals or _____, isn't it?

SPEAKING

4 A 🔊 3.09 | Complete the conversation with one word in each gap. Then listen and check.

Peter: Have you seen that TV programme *The Crown*?
Alex: Yeah. I've watched the first series.
Peter: What's it ¹_____?
Alex: It's about the British Royal Family. Each series concentrates on a different period of time and the events that took place then. It's a ²_____ slow in places for me, but it's interesting enough.
Peter: Does it show real events ³_____ stuff? Or is it all made up?
Alex: It's based on real things that happened, but I think they sort ⁴_____ use a bit of artistic licence – you know, they don't really know what people said ⁵_____ anything so they have to make that up.

B 🔊 3.10 | You are Alex in Ex 4A. Listen and speak after the beep. Record the conversation if you can and compare yourself to Ex 4A.

Speak anywhere   Go to the interactive speaking practice

Lesson 3D

GRAMMAR | *do* and *did* for emphasis
LISTENING | a music podcast

GRAMMAR

do and *did* for emphasis

1 A Choose the correct word to complete the sentences.
1. I really **did / didn't / don't** delete your Spotify account! You must've done it by mistake.
2. I know you think hiking that mountain is possible in a single day but I just **did / don't / do**.
3. Oh, I **do / did / didn't** love this song when I was younger – I would dance to it all the time.
4. I **do / don't / didn't** listen to electronic music – just not the kind that you like!
5. **Do / Does / Don't** come over after the concert if you have time.
6. I **do / didn't / did** use to get up at midday when I was younger, but I don't now!

B Complete the sentences with *do, don't, does, doesn't* or *did*.
1. I .... want to go to the gig, but I just can't afford it right now.
2. Saira does have expensive tastes in clothes, ... she?
3. I .... call the venue to check the gig was still on, but no one answered.
4. You .... remember to send that gift to Mario, didn't you?
5. I loved The Sparks' last two albums, but I really .... like this one.
6. You .... like spaghetti with meatballs, don't you?
7. You .... know I'm not into jazz. I've told you before.
8. He .... like your band, but he just doesn't like crowded places.

LISTENING

2 A 🔊 **3.11** | Listen to the introduction to a music podcast and answer the questions.
1. Which genre are they talking about?
2. Who is Elijah?
3. Who is Bethany?

B 🔊 **3.12** | Listen to the next part of the podcast and choose the correct option (a–c).
1. How does Bethany think some people react when they hear jazz?
   a They feel anxious.
   b They feel annoyed.
   c They feel confused.
2. What does Elijah think puts people off about jazz?
   a the unusual techniques used
   b the sound of certain instruments
   c the lack of real tunes
3. What do Elijah and Bethany agree on?
   a Some kinds of jazz are easier to listen to.
   b People should avoid jazz if they don't like it.
   c Only jazz musicians understand it properly.

C 🔊 **3.12** | Listen to the main part of the podcast again. Complete the sentences with no more than three words from the recording.
1. Bethany says it's hard to know what will happen in jazz because some musicians .... while playing.
2. Bethany says we tend not to like music or other things that make us feel ....
3. Elijah describes a .... called 'noodling', in which the musicians move away from the main tune.
4. Elijah says noodling can seem .... but says that it has structure and tune.
5. Elijah thinks jazz has an .... and shows a lot of creativity.
6. Bethany says that basic and structured jazz makes a .... to jazz music for people.

D 🔊 **3.13** | Listen to the final sentence again and write what you hear. You will hear the sentence only once.

....

Lesson 4A

GRAMMAR | future continuous and future perfect
VOCABULARY | health and lifestyle; illness and treatment
PRONUNCIATION | connected speech: future perfect

VOCABULARY

health and lifestyle

1 Complete the sentences with the correct form of the verbs in the box.

> do (x2)   cut   expand   keep (x2)
> stay   transform   vary   work

1 It's very important, especially as you get older, to .... mentally active. Doing puzzles is great for your brain.
2 I've .... down on the amount of fat and sugar I consume and feel much healthier now.
3 You really need to .... your horizons and get out and about more.
4 It's hard to find time to .... in shape when you've got a full-time job and a family to look after.
5 Research shows that .... regular workouts is good for you both mentally and physically.
6 I .... a sedentary job for years and was very unfit. Then I retrained as a yoga teacher and now I'm healthier than ever!
7 I've always .... long hours and I'm often too tired to make a proper meal when I get home.
8 Last year, my sister totally .... her lifestyle. She became a vegan and started doing more exercise.
9 It's important to .... your diet as much as you can and include all food groups in your meals.
10 I took up running last year and hopefully, if I .... up my progress, I'll do a marathon soon!

illness and treatment

2 A Complete the table with the words in the box.

> allergies   antibiotics   asthma   first aid
> food poisoning   medication   run-down   vaccine

illness	treatment

B Complete the sentences with words to describe illness and treatment.

1 The whole group got .... from the restaurant and were very sick.
2 I suffer from .... all year round and often have itchy eyes and sneeze a lot.
3 I did a .... course so that I could help anyone who suddenly became ill or injured.
4 If you want to find out whether your .... can be taken with other medicines, please consult your doctor.
5 Patients are given .... to help fight against diseases.
6 Sophie's feeling a bit ...., so won't be coming to school today.

GRAMMAR

future continuous and future perfect

3 A The sentences below have a mistake. Choose the best option to correct the mistake.

1 In two years' time <u>I'll be completing</u> my degree and hopefully found a job.
   a I'll have completed   b I'm completing
   c I completed
2 This time next week, <u>you'll have swum</u> in the sea and thinking of me back at home!
   a you'll be swimming   b you'll swim
   c you're swimming
3 If I'm lucky, I'll have got a visa and <u>work</u> in Australia by next summer.
   a I'll work   b working   c be working
4 <u>I'll be finishing</u> lunch by 1 p.m., so we could go for a walk then.
   a I've finished   b I'll have finished   c I finished

B Complete the blog post with the future continuous or future perfect form of the verbs in brackets.

Going Vegan

Going vegan has been a gradual process for me. By this time next month, I'll [1]............... (be) vegan for a whole year.

I became vegetarian first: I'll [2]............... (celebrate) three years without meat or fish next week. It was hard to give up my favourites, but now I barely think about what I no longer eat – only what I'll [3]............... (have) for my next meal! I've become very inventive – you have to be when you're vegan – and I might [4]............... (set up) my own vegan meal business soon.

Personally, I did it because I developed a mild allergy to milk and dairy products, so I had to cut down on them. I'll [5]............... (go) to the doctor's soon and we'll see whether things have improved – I think my allergy will [6]............... (improve) because my symptoms are much better.

There are lots of benefits to going vegan, for both personal benefit and the planet's. If I can convince my parents to go vegan, I'll [7]............... (do) a pretty good job of getting my message across. However, it's important to remember that you may not always get everything you need from a vegan diet – I'll [8]............... (write) a blog soon about the vitamin supplements that can be helpful for staying on top form. Watch this space!

4A

PRONUNCIATION

4 A 🔊 **4.01 | connected speech: future perfect |**
Listen and complete the sentences.

1. By this time next week, _____ this project.
2. Hopefully, _____ meat entirely by then.
3. With any luck, _____ a house by then.
4. Come round at 7 p.m. – _____ dinner by then.
5. By this time next week, _____ from university!

B 🔊 **4.01 |** Listen again and repeat.

READING

5 A Skim the article and choose the main topic (a–c).

a. The benefits of different kinds of diet
b. The reality behind commonly held beliefs
c. The reasons we're lied to about what we eat

B Read the article again. Are the statements True (T) or False (F)?

The writer …

1. thinks food producers try to trick customers into paying too much for food.
2. will continue to buy the expensive health foods that she particularly likes.
3. feels that the message about fat has been very clearly stated.
4. does not intend to limit the amount of high-fat food she eats.
5. is confused about whether or not people should take extra vitamins.
6. has believed information provided on food packaging in the past.

C 📄 Read the article again and answer the questions. Use no more than three words for each answer.

1. What are superfoods meant to stop?
   ....
2. What does the writer think food manufacturers want from people?
   ....
3. What phrase does the writer use to describe the act of labelling food low in fat?
   ....
4. What is the writer happy to continue eating?
   ....

Health myths busted!

We all want to be healthier, but with so much (mis)information out there, it can be difficult to know which changes are actually worth making. So, here is the truth about four common food myths, which may help you make up your mind …

Myth 1: Superfoods are a thing

Sorry, but superfoods *aren't* a thing! Yep, you heard right. While we've all been filling our trolleys with blueberries, ginger and coconut, it turns out that, yes, they do us good, but they're no better than other fruit and veg. 'Super' foods are promoted because they supposedly contain huge amounts of antioxidants (substances that prevent cell damage in our bodies), and the message is that we should buy as many as we can. These (often exotic) foods are – surprise, surprise – very expensive, though. I know what I'll be getting from now on: cheap 'ordinary' veg that I love just as much!

Myth 2: All fat is bad fat

We've been told (over and over again) that we should cut down on foods that contain saturated fats, such as butter, cream and cheese, and eat plenty of foods that are great for heart, eye and brain health (think Omega 3 in oily fish). But the jury seems to be out on whether saturated fats *really* cause heart disease, and whether foods that contain cholesterol (a fat which can be found in eggs) *actually* raise cholesterol in our blood. I think I'll be carrying on with less butter and more salmon, just in case …

Myth 3: You don't need supplements

OK, so this one's hotly debated! Many say that if you have a varied diet, you'll get everything your body needs, and that manufacturers only promote vitamins and supplements so they can fill their pockets with our hard-earned cash! But it turns out there *are* arguments *for* supplements in certain circumstances: those with health conditions including diabetes, pregnant women and people over 50 *can* benefit from additional vitamins. Who knew? 🙊

Myth 4: low fat = low calorie

Nope! It's just another marketing trick! Look in supermarkets and you'll see 'low-fat', 'fat free', 'diet' and 'light' in lots of labels. I've certainly fallen into that trap! While they might truthfully be low in fat, they may also be highly processed and full of sugar to make them tasty. 'You're better off having a few nuts or full-fat items like cheese and yoghurt than eating so-called "diet" products', says one specialist. I, for one, will be following this advice. So, bring on the ice cream (just not too much of it)!

Lesson 4B

GRAMMAR | passives
VOCABULARY | sleep
PRONUNCIATION | sentence stress: content and function words

VOCABULARY

sleep

1 A Complete the conversation with the words in the box.

> deep   dropping off   exhausted   keep
> nightmare   oversleep   sleeper   snore

Doctor: Thanks for coming to the sleep clinic. I'd like to ask you a few questions before we run some tests.

Fran: Sure. I've just been so [1]_____ lately and I don't know why! I go to bed early, but often [2]_____ and end up being late for work.

Doctor: What time do you usually go to bed?

Fran: About ten o'clock. I don't have any problems [3]_____ and I'm never awake past 11 p.m.

Doctor: Do you wake during the night?

Fran: Only if I'm having a [4]_____. But I usually go back to sleep again once I'm calmer.

Doctor: And do you [5]_____? I mean, has anyone ever told you that you do?

Fran: Sometimes – if I've gone to bed *really* tired. I [6]_____ my husband awake then because I'm so loud – so he says! I think I must be quite a heavy [7]_____.

Doctor: Why's that?

Fran: Well, I usually wake up with a headache. When my alarm goes off, it's like I must've been in a really [8]_____ sleep and I struggle to wake up.

Doctor: Well, that doesn't sound good. What we're going to do at the clinic is …

B Choose the correct word or phrase to complete the sentences.

1 I'm _____ – I never wake up, even if there's a thunderclap outside!
   a a heavy sleeper   b an insomniac   c exhausted

2 There was a noisy party last night which _____ us awake.
   a kept   b overslept   c dropped

3 I _____ today – I just didn't hear my alarm.
   a kept awake   b overslept   c lied in

4 She says she always takes a short _____ on the train after work.
   a nap   b nightmare   c snore

5 I rarely get a _____ – my kids are up at dawn practically every day!
   a drop off   b lie-in   c nap

6 My husband says that I _____ and keep him awake at night.
   a oversleep   b drop off   c snore

GRAMMAR

passives

2 Complete the article about sleep disorders using the correct passive form of the verbs in brackets.

Why do people …

… sleepwalk?

It [1]_____ (suggest) that sleepwalking runs in families. If you have a family member who walks in their sleep, it [2]_____ generally _____ (accept) that you are ten times more likely to do it yourself. It [3]_____ also _____ (suspect) that stress, illness and medication can make sleepwalking more likely. It [4]_____ once _____ (assume) to be dangerous to wake a sleepwalker, but this [5]_____ now _____ (not consider) to be a problem. However, it should be done quietly and carefully to keep distress to a minimum.

… talk in their sleep?

Talking in your sleep [6]_____ (define) as a sleep disorder where the sleep-talker doesn't know what they're doing. Speech [7]_____ more easily _____ (understand) when it occurs during REM sleep (when people are dreaming). Anyone can sleep-talk, but it [8]_____ (observe) most often in men and children. Records show that sleep-talking [9]_____ (notice) by ancient Greek philosophers about 2,500 years ago, so it [10]_____ (not discover) recently. Sleep-talking isn't usually a problem and does not require treatment.

PRONUNCIATION

3 A | sentence stress: content and function words | Read the sentences and predict which words will be stressed the most.

1 It was thought that eating cheese before bedtime gives you nightmares.

2 It's been suggested that using your phone in bed makes it harder to drop off.

3 It's believed that up to fifteen percent of the population are sleepwalkers.

4 It's estimated that most people sleep for fewer than seven hours a night.

B 4.02 | Listen and check.

4B

LISTENING

4 A 🔊 **4.03** | Listen to the introduction to a radio programme. What kind of programme is it?

B 🔊 **4.04** | Listen to the next part of the programme and choose the correct option(s) (a–c).
1 What does Rob say about using a sleep tracker?
   a It provided some useful information.
   b It helped him learn to relax.
   c It caused him problems.
2 How did Jenna feel before using her technique?
   a worried about her future
   b scared about being kept awake
   c relieved to get some sleep during the day
3 What does Jenna say helped her sleep better?
   a reading before she went to sleep
   b learning about sleep psychology
   c quitting an old habit
4 What does Álvaro say about nuts?
   a He says they should be avoided at night.
   b He is pleased he can eat more of his favourite kind.
   c He doesn't fully understand how they work.
5 What does Sonya say about the techniques?
   a She finds them quite difficult to do.
   b She thinks they sound rather unusual.
   c She is not very keen to have a go at them.

C 🔊 **4.05** | Listen to the recording and write what you hear. You will hear the sentence only once.

WRITING

an article

5 A Read the article and tick the topics that are mentioned.

> dreams   lack of sleep   napping   nightmares
> sleep and disability   sleep behaviours
> sleep cycles   sleep positions

B Complete the article (1–5) with the sentences (a–e).
   a In addition to this, they can involve anxiety, too.
   b as well as sleep paralysis, where you wake up, but are unable to move.
   c Moreover, their dreams involve feelings, smells and sounds rather than sight.
   d Furthermore, they make friends easily, but don't enjoy being the centre of attention.
   e A lack of sleep not only affects your mental health, but also your physical health.

C You are going to write an article about what kind of sleeper you are. Plan your article. Choose three ideas to write about from Ex 5A.

D Write an article about what kind of sleeper you are.

Six Amazing Facts You Didn't Know About Sleep

Sleep has fascinated experts for centuries and new information is being discovered all the time. So, we've put together six of the most amazing facts we could find on the topic.

- Most nightmares are not frightening. They often include feelings of sadness, guilt and confusion. ¹_____ They happen most often when someone is feeling worried.

- The position you prefer to sleep in *might* reflect your personality. For example, people who sleep on their backs in the 'starfish' position tend to be good listeners. ²_____

- ³_____ For example, you won't cope with pain as well when you don't sleep much.

- Contrary to what some people may think, blind people do dream. ⁴_____ Also, interestingly, deaf people use sign language when they dream.

- Everyone dreams, but they might not remember them. Those that do remember will have forgotten fifty percent of the dream within five minutes of waking. The most common dreams include teeth falling out, forgetting to prepare for an exam, and trying to run but not getting anywhere.

- Some unusual sleep behaviours include parasomnia or making unusual movements in your sleep; 'exploding head syndrome' where someone wakes to a loud noise that is only in their head, ⁵_____ Don't worry if this happens to you – it just means your brain's woken up before the rest of your body has!

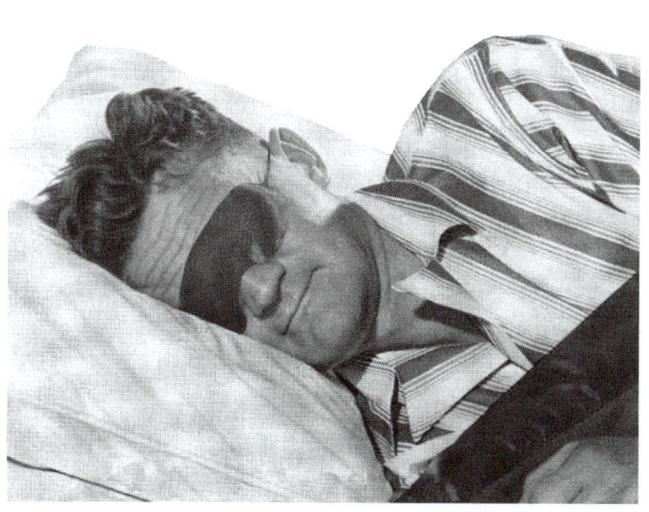

Lesson 4C

HOW TO ... | express agreement and disagreement
VOCABULARY | exercise; sport: motivation and benefits
PRONUNCIATION | stress in phrases for partial agreement

VOCABULARY

exercise

1. Choose the correct word or phrase to complete the sentences.
   1. You need a lot of **flexibility / stamina / moderate exercise** to be able to finish a marathon. They take a long time to run!
   2. It's important to do some **aerobic / low-impact / stamina** exercise because it makes your heart beat faster.
   3. **Strength / Flexibility / Low-impact** training doesn't have to mean hours lifting weights – you can build muscle using your own body weight at home.
   4. An example of **aerobic / high-impact / low-impact** training is yoga, which is gentle but strengthening.
   5. I do **moderate / vigorous / stamina** exercise every day, just a 20-minute walk around the park.
   6. **High-impact / Flexibility / Strength** exercise includes things like running and ball sports, such as football or tennis.

sport: motivation and benefits

2. Complete the fundraising page with the words in the box. There is one word which you do not need.

   > benefit challenge confidence discipline
   > encouragement incentive teamwork

   ## Cycling for the kids!

   £1,258 raised by **3,480 supporters**   **DONATE**

   So, this year I'm planning a huge ¹_____ for myself and I need your ²_____ to get me going!

   I'm going to cycle the length of the country in as short a time as possible. The ³_____ for me to raise money for a children's charity that is close to my heart, and the ⁴_____ to them is being able to fund more research to make lives better.

   I'm going to need a lot of ⁵_____ to make sure I get up early to train before work, even when it's dark or cold. Most of my weekends will be spent cycling long-distance routes. I also need to build my ⁶_____ for cycling bigger roads, though I'll take quieter ones when possible.

   Follow the link to find out more about the charity or donate now.

How to ...

express agreement and disagreement

3. A 4.06 | Listen to a conversation between two friends. What are they talking about?

   B 4.06 | Listen again. Do the friends agree (A), disagree (D) or partially agree (PA) with each other about the statements (1–6)?
   1. Micro-HITT training doesn't seem worth the effort.
   2. One benefit of micro-HITT is that it's quick.
   3. Everesting sounds like a manageable challenge.
   4. New cyclists could cope with Everesting.
   5. The man needs to find a relaxing form of exercise.
   6. Yogalates helps with physical and mental health.

PRONUNCIATION

4. A 4.07 | **stress in phrases for partial agreement** | Listen and underline the main stressed word in each of the phrases in bold.
   1. **I agree up to a point**, but don't you think the government should play a role, too?
   2. **I take your point**, but that's what footballers expect to get paid.
   3. **That's a fair point**, but don't you think they get enough exercise at school?

   B 4.07 | Listen again and repeat the sentences.

SPEAKING

5. A 4.08 | Complete the conversation with phrases for agreeing and disagreeing. Then listen and check.

   Marla: Let's do something. It would be a shame to stay in on a day like this.
   Dan: I ¹_____ more. What shall we do? Want to try bouldering with me? Come on …
   Marla: Climbing over massive rocks all day? No, thanks. It sounds exhausting.
   Dan: I know what ²_____, but you did say you want to improve your strength a bit …
   Marla: That's a fair ³_____, but I've got work tomorrow and I don't want to be worn out.
   Dan: You go to the gym all the time – you'll be fine!
   Marla: I completely ⁴_____! Last time we went jogging it took me a week to recover!
   Dan: All right. I take ⁵_____. You do need a lot of stamina. But on the ⁶_____, if you stay here all day, you'll never get fitter!

   B 4.09 | You are Dan in the conversation in Ex 5A. Listen and speak after the beep. Record the conversation if you can.

   C Listen to your recording and compare it to Ex 5A.

Speak anywhere Go to the interactive speaking practice

Lesson 4D

VOCABULARY | phrases related to time
READING | disappearing traditional skills and lifestyles

VOCABULARY

phrases related to time

1 Choose the correct option(s) to complete the sentences.
1 **Time is running out / It's time to move on** for endangered animals and we need to take action.
2 We got to the theatre **just in time / not a moment too soon** for the start of the play.
3 We've got a very short **future under threat / window of opportunity** to carry out the conservation project.
4 I've got some new boots and **time is running out / not a moment too soon** – the old ones were wearing out!
5 The future of our planet **is still under threat / has a short window of opportunity** and we must keep making changes to our habits.
6 **It's just in time for / It's time to move on from** this job. I've become very bored.
7 The community are increasingly concerned that their traditional way of life is **under threat / running out**.
8 Right, I think it's probably **just in time / time** to go home or I'll miss the last train!

READING

2 A Read the article. What is its purpose?

B Read the article again. Are the statements True (T) or False (F)?
1 Kerry does not believe readers are aware of the skill practised by her great-grandfather.
2 Kerry suggests that people who wore clogs could not afford to replace them regularly.
3 Nisse says that Franco-Provençal speakers moved out to the countryside from cities.
4 Nisse speaks a different language to his grandparents because he does not need to use the language they speak.
5 Özkan believes that the way people worked in the past used a lot of time and energy.
6 Özkan ithinks that technology can only solve one kind of problem.
7 Agata is not impressed with her grandparents' lifestyle choice.
8 Agata would be happy to move on from every aspect of traditional life.

Should we care about losing traditional skills and ways of life?

Do you know how to make bread? Or fix a hole in your socks? Or even how to light a fire? For all too many of us, the answer to all of these questions is 'no'. Basic life skills that were once a staple part of everyday life have all but disappeared. But is this a bad thing?

YES!

Kerry, UK: My great-grandad used to make clogs. I bet you don't even know what they are! Well, they're shoes made from leather and wood. They last a long time. This is why they were chosen by low-paid workers who put in long days at cotton mills, in coal mines and on boats that transported goods along canals. A very limited number of clog-makers still exist, but their future is under threat, as so few people wear clogs now. It would be a shame if such a great skill – and fantastic style of footwear – disappeared forever.

Nisse, Switzerland: Time is running out for my grandparents' language, Franco-Provençal. They live in an isolated part of Switzerland, and because my parents (like many) moved away to find work, I never learned it. Now it's dying out, despite attempts to get people learning it. I understand it, but I only speak Swiss-German – the most common language in Switzerland. Lots of books used to be written in Franco-Provençal. The window of opportunity for reviving the language is short. If no one can speak it, how will we learn about the history of our country?

NO!

Özkan, Turkey: People make a lot of fuss about 'lost' skills and ways of life. But if they were so good in the first place, why did they disappear? It's time to move on. My grandparents lived tough lives as farmers, using traditional skills – but only because that's what was available then. It wasn't considered 'traditional' at the time! As far as I can tell, traditional skills and ways of life were very hard. Technology has solved so many problems and many people are a lot better off in all kinds of ways – not just financially, but health- and time-wise, too.

Agata, Poland: When I visit my great-grandparents in their village, I feel like I've gone back in time by a century. I suppose I have in a way because they stick to the 'old ways' and don't live as comfortably and easily as they could do – well, that's only my opinion. They don't enjoy using modern technology, anyway! For me, when a new app or phone model comes out, it's not a moment too soon. I will say this, though: I always seem to arrive just in time when my great-grandma's cooked some traditional dumplings – delicious! That way of life should never disappear!

3-4 REVIEW

GRAMMAR

1 Combine the sentences using a relative clause. Omit the pronoun where possible.

1 Nick works at the theatre. The one over there.
   That's _____ works.
2 We met a girl at your cousin's barbecues. Is that her?
   Is that _____ your cousin's barbecue?
3 A guy got his car stuck in the mud. I think that's him over there.
   I think that's _____ got stuck in the mud.
4 The venue has been very successful. It opened last year.
   The venue, _____, has been very successful.
5 Remember the hotel we stayed in for our honeymoon? They closed it!
   They closed _____ in for our honeymoon!

2 Match the sentence beginnings (1–6) with the endings (a–f).

1 It was Felicity   a is wash your hands.
2 What I want to know   b who told me.
3 It's Helena that   c do is go to sleep!
4 It was Ankoma who   d is what you were doing!
5 What you need to do   e told everyone.
6 What I'd like to   f you need to speak to.

3 Complete the conversation with the correct form of *do* to add emphasis.

A: Are you going to the company party on Thursday?
B: I ¹_____ want to go but it's on the other side of London from me. It'll be fun, though.
A: Hmm, well, I didn't want to go last year either but I must admit, I ²_____ enjoy it in the end.
B: Yes, and there's a DJ again, isn't there?
A: Well, you ³_____ love a good dance, but I really ⁴_____! I hate it.
B: Fair enough. The quiz should be good though. I think Emir's running it this year.
A: Well, he ⁵_____ like testing us all, doesn't he?
B: That's true. I'm rubbish at quizzes but I ⁶_____ like the theme last time – 90s pop music.
A: My team won! I think Mike was unhappy – he ⁷_____ like to show off his knowledge!

4 Complete the text with the future continuous or future perfect forms of the verbs in brackets.

We'll no doubt ¹_____ (hear) more and more weather forecasts about violent storms and flooding. The sad thing is that we probably ²_____ (get used to) such reports by then. And that will only be if we still *have* weather reporters: scientists believe that as well as the weather having become more extreme, our society may also ³_____ (fall) apart by 2050! By 2050, the South Pole ⁴_____ (shrink) considerably, sea levels ⁵_____ (rise) by 30 cm, temperatures ⁶_____ (increase) dramatically, and civilisation as we know it ⁷_____ (start) to collapse. The worst thing is that we ⁸_____ (do) it all to ourselves: it will be our own fault.

5 The sentences below have a mistake. Choose the best option to correct the mistake.

1 <u>There is</u> generally accepted that film-making is a serious form of art.
   a It's   b It was   c There are
2 What's Going On by Marvin Gaye <u>is consider to be</u> one of the best albums of all time.
   a is considered being   b considers being
   c is considered to be
3 In the late 1800s, <u>they believe widely</u> that the Earth was flat.
   a it's widely believe   b it was widely believed
   c they widely believe it
4 Despite evidence to the contrary, Vitamin C <u>thought still is</u> to cure the common cold.
   a still are thinking   b it's still thought
   c is still thought

VOCABULARY

6 Choose the correct words to complete the sentences.

1 The **line-up / act** for the festival is superb, with over 50 bands performing over the weekend.
2 The **festival-goers / atmosphere** at music festivals is always amazing.
3 I think the **organisers / festival-goers** have done a great job of the layout.
4 Sanjay's never **attended / attracted** a festival before so we should look after him.
5 Donauinselfest is the world's biggest music festival, **attending / attracting** three million people!

7 Complete the sentences with the words in the box.

| emissions   footprint   power   recycling   resources |

1 In an effort to reduce their carbon _____ music festivals are going greener.
2 Lollapalooza has it own programme to encourage festival-goers to do more _____.
3 Reducing the number of plastic bottles that are made can help lower carbon _____ from the factories that produce them.
4 Many people who attend the Paléo Festival in Switzerland use public transport to avoid unnecessary use of natural _____.
5 At the We Love Green festival in France, festival-goers can generate _____ by cycling at the festival's 'electric pedals' station.

8 Replace the words in bold with the correct form of the phrasal verbs in the box.

| come up with   fall back on   live up to
  mess up   put someone off |

1 I've **thought of** a brilliant idea for a new play.
2 You should stay at uni so you have something else to **use** if the band doesn't work out.
3 Your act was incredible – how can I ever **be as good as** that?

30

REVIEW 3–4

4 I **got** all my lines **wrong** on stage – it was really embarrassing.

5 Stop making silly faces – you're **distracting** me.

9 Complete the phrasal verbs with *across, back, on to, out* or *up*.

1 You come .... as such a friendly person, but you're actually quite mean!
2 OK, let's move .... to the issue of parking for the event.
3 Can you speak .... a bit, please? We can't hear you at the back.
4 I'll come .... to the topic of recycling later, if I may.
5 My teacher spelled .... exactly what we had to do for our homework.

10 Complete the sentences with the words in the box.

| based on   costumes   ending   soundtrack   twist |

1 I was totally confused by the .... – why did they finish it off like that?
2 The .... were amazing in that film. I'd love to wear something like that.
3 I enjoyed it but the .... was weird. It was set in 1770, but they used punk rock!
4 Is the series .... a true story?
5 Wow, what a .... ! I didn't see that coming!

11 Choose the correct words to complete the tips.

If you want to ¹**transform / expand** your lifestyle, follow our top tips!

If you do a ²**sedentary / active** job, you need to make sure you build exercise into your day. If you can do a ³**sedentary / regular** workout, even better! It can be difficult to ⁴**stay / do** in shape when you work ⁵**active / long** hours, but exercising when you can makes all the difference.

Try to ⁶**expand / transform** your horizons: sign up for a new activity like high-intensity pool training.

Change what you eat: make sure you ⁷**cut down on / vary** your diet and ⁸**expand / cut down** on fatty and sugary foods.

⁹**Keep / Work** mentally active, too. Do puzzles, dance – anything to help your brain stay sharp.

Finally, ¹⁰**stay in / keep up** the progress! Once you see the rewards of your efforts, you'll be keen to remain your best self.

12 Complete the definitions with the words in the box.

| allergies   antibiotics   asthma
  food poisoning   medication |

1 .... : medical conditions that make you ill when you eat, breathe or touch something.
2 .... : a stomach illness caused by eating food that contains harmful bacteria.
3 .... : an illness that makes it difficult to breathe.

4 .... : drugs that are used to kill bacteria and cure infections.
5 .... : a drug given to someone who is ill.

13 Choose the correct word or phrase to complete the sentences.

1 I'm such a .... sleeper that I don't even wake up with a really loud alarm.
  a light   b heavy   c weak
2 My wife's .... and she disturbs me when she puts the light on when she can't sleep.
  a an insomniac   b a deep sleeper   c a snorer
3 I usually .... pretty quickly at night but wake up a few hours later.
  a deep sleep   b drop off   c nap
4 My dad always has a .... after lunch. Eating seems to make him tired.
  a nap   b lie-in   c nightmare
5 I love having a .... at the weekends, but I get up early the rest of the week.
  a deep sleep   b snore   c lie-in
6 My daughter woke me up at 1 a.m. She'd had a .... and couldn't go back to sleep.
  a nightmare   b lie-in   c snore

14 Complete the sentences with the words in the box.

| aerobic   flexibility   moderate   stamina   vigorous |

1 It's better to do a small amount of .... exercise every day than to do a lot of exercise on one occasion and then do nothing for weeks.
2 You really only need to do 20 minutes of .... exercise a day, such as a gentle walk.
3 I'm currently building my .... to do a marathon next month.
4 I really enjoy .... exercise like dancing and running.
5 I really need to improve my .... – I can barely touch my toes.

15 Choose the correct words to complete the sentences.

1 There's no real **incentive / discipline** for me to do more exercise. I'm fit enough.
2 I'll admit that winning is my main **motivation / confidence** when it comes to competitive sport.
3 I think playing in a team really boosted my **confidence / challenge**.
4 You need a high level of **benefit / discipline** to become a good gymnast or dancer.
5 I like a **challenge / motivation**, so I'm going to do an ultra-marathon next year.

16 Complete the sentences with the words *time, future, moment* or *opportunity*.

1 The .... of the giant panda no longer seems to be under threat.
2 It's .... to get real about online security. We have to take it more seriously.
3 Action is finally being taken to improve air quality – and not a .... too soon.
4 We have a small window of .... in which to slow the rate of global warming.
5 .... is running out for endangered species.

31

Lesson 5A

GRAMMAR | past perfect simple and continuous
VOCABULARY | time expressions
PRONUNCIATION | connected speech: past perfect continuous

VOCABULARY

time expressions

1 A Complete the conversation with the phrases in the box.

> by the time   for ages   for a while   in no time
> just moments earlier   up to that point

Adam: Have you ever done any of those embarrassing ice-breaker activities at work?

Isha: Yeah, I did one last year. We were asked to find the person in the room we had most in common with. ¹_____ I'd finally understood what we were doing, most people had already paired up. ²_____, I'd just been going round introducing myself! We'd been given the instructions ³_____, but I was chatting away ⁴_____ and forgot the purpose of the whole thing. I ended up on my own! What about you?

Adam: I haven't done any ⁵_____, but my friend has just reminded me of some we did in our language class. We did this 'speed meeting' activity, introducing ourselves to as many people as we could in five minutes. ⁶_____, I'd realised how much work I had to do on my English – at least that made me study harder!

B Choose the correct phrase to complete the sentences.

1 I hadn't done an interview **up to that point / for a while / in no time** and I'd forgotten how to prepare properly.
2 My boss had told me her name **just moments earlier / for ages / up to that point** but I'd completely forgotten it.
3 **By the time / In no time / For a while** we'd all introduced ourselves, the meeting was almost over.
4 I couldn't get in and had to wait **for ages / just moments / up to that point** to be let in.
5 I had my first call with the team in China today! **By the time / In no time / Up to that point** I'd only spoken to them via email.
6 I feel really comfortable in my new job and I made friends **for ages / in no time / for a while**.

GRAMMAR

past perfect simple and continuous

2 A The sentences below have a mistake. Choose the best option to correct the mistake.

1 I got halfway to work and realised <u>I'd been leaving</u> my lunch in the fridge!
   a I was leaving   b I'd been left   c I'd left
2 <u>I'd waited</u> for an hour before they finally called me to my interview.
   a I'd been waiting   b I'd been waited
   c I been waiting
3 When I finally got to the conference, the talk I wanted to see <u>finished</u>.
   a had been finishing   b had finished   c finishing
4 I <u>tried</u> for hours before someone finally answered the phone.
   a am trying   b 'd been trying   c 've been trying

B Choose the correct phrase to complete the sentences.

Newbie123   23 April at 23:45
I've just had my first ever day at work!!!! By the time my line manager ¹_____ (introduce) me to everyone and given me a tour of the office, it was time for lunch. I ²_____ (never see) an office canteen before and was amazed at the choice of food – yum! In the afternoon, I ³_____ (work) on the newsletter for a while when my manager invited me to go to a meeting with my favourite TV actor! Most. Awesome. Day. Ever.

ManagementPro   20th April at 01:32
So, I've just got a promotion! I ⁴_____ (prepare) for weeks for the interview so I was pleased that it went smoothly. The scary thing is that I'm now managing a team for the first time. I immediately got lots of emails asking me questions! I ⁵_____ (forgot) how demanding people can be. Anyway, I ⁶_____ (spend) an hour or so looking through them when a really nice one dropped into my inbox – 'Welcome to our team!'

WindDownWorker   19th April at 11:39
I'm really getting ready for retirement now. I ⁷_____ (already reduce) my working hours to three days and I ⁸_____ (look forward to) that for ages. Now I've gone down to just two. Now I've got time to put my energies into other things – like playing sport and doing some volunteering. I ⁹_____ (always planned) to set up my own small business when I retired, but having enjoyed a taste of freedom, I've decided against that!

5A

PRONUNCIATION

3 A 🔊 5.01 | connected speech: past perfect continuous |
Listen and complete the sentences.
1 They _____ outside for hours.
2 I _____ for new job.
3 She _____ for a while.
4 _____ before that?
5 _____ at the bus stop for ages.
6 The team _____ for a pay rise for months.

B 🔊 5.01 | Listen again and repeat the sentences as fluently as possible.

READING

4 A You're going to read an article about what young people expect from the modern workplace. Read the title, tagline and subheadings and predict what each section will be about.

B Read the article and check your ideas.

C Which of the people in the article say the following?
1 We are very accepting of people from all different backgrounds. _____
2 Older generations think we are wasting our time with a certain activity. _____
3 Messing up provides an opportunity for learning. _____
4 We find quicker ways of doing things at work. _____
5 Previous generations were probably bothered by inequality but didn't show it. _____
6 We know we are easily capable of solving problems. _____
7 We're happy that certain measures are in place to look after employees. _____
8 We should take responsibility for the things we do wrong. _____

Gen Z – tech-loving, inclusive and flexible

Is the workplace ready for the next generation?

TECHNOLOGY
Alex, 21

'We've become known as the generation who's always stuck to our phones ignoring the world around us. But all along, we've been using those phones to learn and soak up information. We are brilliant at networking and have loads of connections. Stop and consider how useful that can be to a company. Technology doesn't scare us like it did previous generations – we embrace new digital concepts and products and can help companies advance. Technology had been around since long before we were born and it's the norm for us to make use of it. We're ready to meet challenges because we know we've got the resources at our fingertips.'

DIVERSITY AND INCLUSION
Elliott, 18

'Diversity. That's what we want from our workplace. And inclusion. We want our differences to be acknowledged and welcomed. In my opinion, our parents and grandparents had got so used to dealing with discrimination in the workplace that they didn't do enough to change it. When it comes to my generation, we want to make sure no one's discriminated against for any reason and will stand up for what we believe in. There's no room for prejudice or exclusion. We don't judge and nor should you.'

RESPONSIBILITY
Jitka, 19

'I think it's crucial for companies and individuals to take responsibility for their actions and resolve any errors of judgement. I think our generation understands that we have to be accountable for the things we've done – or not done. You know, I mean, we expect everyone to own their mistakes. We don't like the idea of blaming other people for mistakes either. We strongly believe in learning from our mistakes and striving every day to be a better person.'

FLEXIBILITY
Alonzo, 22

'Gen Z is used to the virtual world and we'll be happy to work virtually, too. Traditionally, colleagues emailed each other when they needed a quick reply. But we're more likely to text and use chat and instant messaging. What I'm saying is that we're less formal than the generations before us and that's what we'd like from our places of work, too. I'm not saying rules and regulations should be thrown out of the window – not at all because they're there to protect workers – but does it really matter whether we're wearing a suit and tie when we're programming software from home? We don't expect others to change, but we don't want to be changed either!'

Lesson 5B

GRAMMAR | past plans and intentions
VOCABULARY | work and careers; areas of work
PRONUNCIATION | connected speech: intrusive /w/ sounds

VOCABULARY

work and careers

1 A Choose the correct word or phrase to complete the sentences.

1 I'm thinking of **retraining / reinventing / advancing** myself as a circus performer – what do you think?
2 Ben's done so well since he **switched / started out / set up** at the bank that he's just been promoted.
3 My dad **advanced / switched / retrained** careers in his 50s – it's never too late to make a change.
4 My best friend is **an entrepreneur / part-time / reinventing** – she made this amazing app that lets you sell old clothes.
5 I'd love to **start out / set up / retrain** a company, but I don't know if I've got the right business skills.
6 He'd like to **switch / advance / retrain** his music career by joining a well-known orchestra.

B Complete the text with the correct form of the words in the box.

> advance   entrepreneur   part-time   reinvent
> retrain   set up   start out   switch

Switching things up

Aneena Chaudri   Wednesday 20th Aug | 11.44 GMT

We've all had moments where we've thought about changing careers, but what is it like to actually take the plunge? We speak to someone who has successfully ¹_____ himself.

Carlo Voccoli, 39

'I studied Maths at university and ²_____ as a private tutor, helping school students study for exams. I enjoyed working with young people, but the job I had was only ³_____ and I didn't have enough work. I didn't really fancy ⁴_____ as a high school teacher, so I decided to go into accountancy instead. ⁵_____ careers was a positive move for me financially, though I did miss the contact with my students. But I've been ⁶_____ well and I really enjoy being able to use my love of numbers. One day, I wouldn't mind ⁷_____ my own company. I'm no ⁸_____, though, so I'd probably need a partner who knows more about business than I do!'

areas of work

2 Complete the sentences with the words in the box.

> accountancy   agriculture   banking
> construction   consultancy   journalism
> medicine   publishing   research   social work

1 My family has worked in _____ for generations, but farming isn't my thing.
2 I think _____ must be very rewarding – helping people who are in need is so important.
3 My niece wants to do scientific _____ and help find solutions to environmental problems.
4 Employment in the _____ industry has increased rapidly over the last few years, as there has been greater demand for housing.
5 Good _____ is essential in this day and age as there's so much fake news on the internet.
6 _____ can be a tough career because you not only help make people better but have to see people suffering, too.
7 My friend works in a business _____, advising large firms on how to manage change.
8 The _____ industry has changed radically, as more and more people are choosing to read content online rather than buying a book or magazine.
9 _____ is seen as a stable profession – people will always need a secure place to keep their money.
10 To work in _____, you obviously need a good understanding of financial data.

GRAMMAR

past plans and intentions

3 Choose the correct word or phrase to complete the sentences.

1 I **hope / was hoping / has hoped** to become a journalist but ended up in marketing.
2 I **was arranging / arrange / had arranged** to go shopping with my sister, so we met up after work.
3 Ken **was planning / has planned / is planning** to decorate the dining room on Sunday, but he didn't have time in the end.
4 Maja **was considering / is considering / had considered** studying politics, but she's opted for history instead.
5 They **finally deciding / were finally deciding / had finally decided** where to go camping and set off early to avoid traffic.
6 Mel **is always intending / had always intended / always intends** to go into banking and she found a job straight after college.

5B

PRONUNCIATION

4 A 🔊 5.02 | connected speech: intrusive /w/ sounds |
Draw a line ⌣ between words which are connected with an intrusive /w/ sound. Then listen and check.

1 I was supposed to open a student bank account today, but I forgot.
2 I was going to ask whether you could help me write a new CV.
3 I was going to advise you against going self-employed.
4 I was meant to email my application form, but I got distracted.
5 I'd love to own a business one day, but I'm not sure what yet.

B 🔊 5.02 | Now listen again and repeat.

LISTENING

5 A 🔊 5.03 | You will hear four people talking about their childhood ambitions. Which speaker is least happy about how things have turned out?

B 🔊 5.03 | Listen again. Are the statements True (T) or False (F)?

1 Mark is unsure why law appealed to him so much.
2 He had an idea of which area of law he wanted to work in when he entered the profession.
3 The reality of Mark's and Amanda's jobs is different to what people might think.
4 Amanda has always thought it would be easy to become a footballer.
5 Chilemba applied for the role because he had experience of working in a similar field.
6 He says that the reality of his job is very different to what to people expect.
7 Kiku says that jobs that children used to want to do largely no longer exist.
8 She says that her kind of role is becoming more popular.

C 🔊 5.04 | Listen to the recording and write what you hear. You will hear the sentence only once.

_____
_____

WRITING

a report

6 A Complete the sentences with the words in the box.

| appears conclude outlines purpose |
| recommended slight sum up |

1 It is .... that young people consider a wide range of career options.
2 The .... of this report is to compare the most popular career choices for university leavers.
3 There has been a .... decrease in the number of people entering social media jobs this year.
4 I .... that getting early careers' advice can be highly beneficial to school-leavers.
5 This report .... the changing trends in workplace layouts over the last decade.
6 It .... that staff absence is reduced when employees have the option of remote working.

B Read the information about remote working. Is it in favour of or against the trend?

Mega-trend: the rise and rise of remote-working

- Office working is under threat from remote-working
- Younger generations prefer a more flexible approach to working environments.
- New software is making remote-working much more possible.
- Most home-workers are in high-skilled and professional jobs.
- Businesses need to support remote-workers (by providing software, home office equipment, etc.).

Benefits to employees:
- allows better work-life balance
- people are happier
- a less competitive environment

Benefits to employers:
- staff work harder
- people stay longer at the company
- better carbon footprint

C Your manager has asked you to write a report comparing remote working and office-based roles and to make recommendations about future positions. Make notes under the following headings:

1 Introduction   3 Main Issues
2 Background   4 Conclusion

D Write your report using your notes and the information in Ex 6B to help you.

Lesson 5C

HOW TO ... | describe problems and suggest solutions
VOCABULARY | video conference calls
PRONUNCIATION | intonation to show degrees of certainty

VOCABULARY

video conference calls

1 A Choose the correct word to complete the sentences.

1 I need to turn the .... up because I can't hear you.
   a echo   b volume   c delay
2 I'm always forgetting to .... myself and no one can hear me speaking.
   a unmute   b unfreeze   c mute
3 I've accepted your .... to the meeting but I don't seem to have the right link.
   a host   b connection   c invite
4 I think Jay's lost his .... He seems to have disappeared from the call.
   a internet connection   b delay   c link
5 Can you type that in the .... so I can check the spelling?
   a link   b invite   c chat box

B Complete the article about video conferencing with the correct form of the words in the box.

> a link   be frozen   delay   get into   host   on mute

Video conferencing for fun

Virtual get-togethers

Carolina's away on business, Mike's got a cold he doesn't want to spread, and Ali's on a long-distance train journey. But they still want their weekly chat. Sure, there may be sound ¹..............., and there will be lots of times when you ²............... on screen with a silly expression on your face, but you don't have to miss out on the fun.

Watching weddings

If you can't get to a wedding because you live halfway across the world, you can still be a guest by being invited to attend online. One click on ³............... and you'll ⁴............... the venue virtually, from thousands of kilometres away.

Games nights

Compete with family and friends who live in different areas by tuning in to live online quizzes. Why not take it in turns to be the ⁵............... of the meeting – and you get to choose the quiz! ☺ Don't forget to put yourself ⁶..............., so other teams can't hear you discussing your answers!

How to ...

describe problems and suggest solutions

2 A 🔊 5.05 | Listen to parts of three video calls. What is the problem in each conversation? What solution is suggested? Make notes.

B 🔊 5.06 | Complete the extracts. Then listen and check.

1 There .... a problem with the mute button.
2 Why .... using your headphones instead?
3 I've clicked on the 'share screen' button. Hmm, I can't get it ....
4 .... leave the meeting for a second or two.
5 Perhaps you .... turning your volume down.
6 It's .... try because it sometimes gets rid of it.

PRONUNCIATION

3 A 🔊 5.07 | **intonation to show degrees of certainty** | Listen to the sentences. Which speakers feel certain about what they are saying?

1 Perhaps you could log off and log in again?
2 You could try sending the link again.
3 It might be worth sharing your screen.
4 It sometimes helps if you turn your camera off.
5 That might work if you haven't already tried it.

B 🔊 5.07 | Listen again and repeat.

SPEAKING

4 A Put the conversation in the correct order.

Sally: Well, we've got a load of jobs to do around the house today. There seems to be a problem with the washing machine. It's not emptying.

Alfie: It might be worth a try ...

Alfie: Oh, dear. Maybe you could find a number for a plumber while I take a quick look. I doubt I'll be able to fix it, though.

Alfie: Good idea. Actually, I can't get the games console working.

Alfie: How's it going?

Sally: Why don't you try taking it to that repair guy?

Sally: Sure. There's something wrong with my bike brakes as well. I'll try replacing the brake pads. That might work because I'm sure they're pretty old now.

B 🔊 5.08 | Now listen and check.

C 🔊 5.09 | You are Sally in Ex 4A. Listen and speak after the beep. Record the conversation if you can.

D Listen to your recording and compare it to the model in Ex 4B.

Speak anywhere Go to the interactive speaking practice

Lesson 5D

GRAMMAR | non-defining relative clauses for comments
LISTENING | team building

GRAMMAR

non-defining relative clauses for comments

1 A Complete the comments with *who*, *which*, *whose*, *where* or *when*.

1 No one in the team would help me finish the report, ... was really annoying!
2 Let me introduce you to your line manager, ... you will work closely with.
3 Your desk is over there by the window, ... you'll have a great view over the city.
4 Why don't we have the meeting on Friday afternoon, ... everyone's a bit more relaxed?
5 If you want to know how the printers work, ask Jo, ... knowledge of them is incredible!
6 I worked on my own in my last job, ... was boring and lonely.

B Complete the text with relative pronouns.

Do you prefer working on your own or as part of a team? Why?

Comments

Helena Yesterday at 10.37
I work as a freelance editor, [1]................. I really enjoy. I work on my own most of the day but I'm also part of a wider team of freelancers [2]................. work together on interesting projects. So, I do a bit of both and I like that!

David Yesterday at 10.41
I work in a sports retail outlet, [3]................. I have a lot of fun chatting to customers and finding things they need. But I'm also part of a team [4]................. main objective is to meet sales targets! That can be tough but on the whole, I like being a team member.

Jacques Yesterday at 10.46
I enjoy working in a team [5]................. the people are nice and we all get on. Unfortunately, I've worked in teams that aren't so great, [6]................. I didn't enjoy at all. At those times, I'd rather have worked on my own.

LISTENING

2 A 🔊 5.10 | Listen to a radio programme about team building. What activities did the three teams do virtually? Make notes.

B 🔊 5.10 | Listen again and choose the correct options (a–c).

1 What does the presenter say about traditional team-building exercises?
   a There were clear favourites amongst employees.
   b Participants came together in the same place.
   c They are no longer used successfully.

2 What do employers now have to consider?
   a how to bring home-working teams together physically
   b how to ensure people working remotely still feel like a team.
   c how to provide a sense of competition between teams

3 What does the first manager say about the escape room activity?
   a It involved a strict time limit.
   b It provided useful feedback.
   c It was particularly challenging.

4 What happened during the travel challenge?
   a Participants felt too much pressure to succeed.
   b Participants needed to do some research.
   c Participants had to do physical activity.

5 What does the third manager say about the murder mystery?
   a It made staff feel happier about their jobs.
   b It encouraged real collaboration.
   c It was straightforward to solve.

6 What does the presenter want listeners to do?
   a Get in touch with suggestions for activities.
   b Research possible team-building activities.
   c Try the activities mentioned on the show.

Lesson 6A

GRAMMAR | necessity, prohibition and permission
VOCABULARY | prefixes
PRONUNCIATION | word stress: prefixes

VOCABULARY

prefixes

1A Complete the conversations with the prefixes in the box.

> dis   im   mis   re   sub   un

1. A: I'm afraid the latest project you handed in is .... standard and you'll need to revise it thoroughly.
   B: I'm sorry, I think I completely .... understood your instructions.
2. A: I'm going to .... do my essay before I hand it in. I've forgotten to include any references.
   B: Well, don't spend too long making .... necessary changes.
3. A: Please don't .... connect my phone. I'm charging it now because it's .... practical to try and do it on a busy train.
   B: Sure.

B Complete the article by adding the correct prefixes to the words in bold.

Can't concentrate on your work? Try the 'Pomodoro' technique

If you're becoming ¹........... patient with your inability to 'get things done', you might want to ²........... train your brain. Telling yourself to manage your time better is ³........... realistic. But the Pomodoro (tomato) technique, developed by Italian business consultant Francesco Cirillo, has is a successful way of being more productive. No, you didn't ⁴........... read the name: Cirillo used a kitchen timer in the shape of a tomato to help him get more done!

The idea is to break work down into 25-minute chunks (using any timer you like!), take a 5-minute break between each one, and repeat throughout the workday. It may sound ⁵........... helpful when you've got a lot to do, and the technique probably is ⁶........... perfect when working on large, complicated projects. But, when it works, it works well: the quality of your work will improve, meaning less ⁷........... writing of work that you've done when you're distracted, and you'll get a better understanding of what might be achievable in the time you've got.

PRONUNCIATION

2A | **word stress: prefixes** | Underline the stressed syllable in the words in bold.

1. I'm usually quite an **impatient** person, but in my work as a teacher, I'm very understanding.
2. Who **disconnected** my laptop? I was charging it for later.
3. I've **rewritten** this paragraph three times already and I'm tired of doing it now!
4. I have poor concentration, so working in an open-plan office is **impractical** for me.
5. I'm afraid this report is **substandard** and it will need to be revised.

B 🔊 6.01 | Listen and check.

GRAMMAR

necessity, prohibition and permission

3A Choose the correct word or phrase to complete the sentences.

1. My hair needed **to cut** / **cutting** / **to have been cut**, so I went to the hairdresser's.
2. Football **Is** / **Isn't** / **Is to be** permitted in the park, so we play at the football pitch instead.
3. My brothers and I were allowed **staying** / **stay** / **to stay** out until it went dark when we were kids.
4. The thief was forbidden to **leave** / **have left** / **leaving** the country and his passport was taken away from him.
5. Something needs **done** / **to do** / **to be done** about all the rubbish people leave in the streets.
6. You are allowed **to have taken** / **to take** / **taking** a dictionary into the exam.

B Complete the sentences with the correct form of the verbs in brackets.

1. The front lawn .... (need / cut) if you've got time.
2. Sorry, photography .... (be / permit) in the gallery.
3. Just a reminder that swimming .... (be / allow) anywhere on the nature reserve.
4. I think this PC .... (need / look at) by one of the technicians.
5. Feeding the animals .... (not / forbid), but all food must be purchased in the shop.
6. Camera flashes .... (not / allow) during the performance.
7. My parents .... (allow) me .... (stay) up late when I was younger.
8. The school .... (permit) students to leave early for doctor's appointments only.

READING

4A Read the first paragraph of the article. What is 'flow'?
  a having good concentration skills
  b getting lots of necessary jobs done
  c being completely focused on an activity

B Read the rest of the article and answer the questions.
  1 Which two conditions for achieving flow during an activity are mentioned? (para 2)
  2 What may people not pay attention to while they are in flow? (para 2)
  3 What words are used to describe getting more done? (para 3)
  4 What phrase is used to describe a sense of calm, which is needed to achieve flow? (para 3)
  5 What do you need to make sure there are few of when trying to achieve flow? (para 3)

The state of 'flow'

[1] We know by now that multi-tasking doesn't work. It's more productive to concentrate on one thing at a time. But what happens when we're concentrating so much that we don't notice what's going on around us? Psychologist Amy Wright discusses this state of mind, which is known as 'flow'.

[2] Flow occurs when you're doing something you really enjoy and are probably fairly good at, such as playing a musical instrument, writing, or even playing sports. Your entire focus is on the task at hand and you often don't notice what's happening around you. You might not 'hear' people having a conversation or notice other noises or activity around you. Once you've finished, you might be left with the feeling that time has flown and that the task didn't take very long at all, when it actually took many minutes or hours. Research shows that this occurs because of changes in brain activity that take place during flow, when an increased level of dopamine – the 'feel-good' chemical – floods the brain.

[3] There are many benefits to flow, from increased attention, to learning and skills development, being more efficient and de-stressing. It leads to greater creativity, motivation, and even happiness. But when does it happen? Flow has several characteristics, and for you to get into the state, you need to experience all of them, though not necessarily all at the same time. The characteristics of an activity include being rewarding, having achievable goals, allowing you to feel in control, and giving you peace of mind. We need to make sure distractions are reduced and that there is some challenge involved, too.

[4] Flow can be achieved in many areas of life, including in creative hobbies, sports, work and education. The good news is that you don't have to just wait for it to come along. Flow can be practised until you achieve it. Keep increasing the challenge and skill level required in your chosen activity, and your state of flow will follow.

WRITING

editing notes

5A Read two sets of notes about the second paragraph of *The state of 'flow'*. Which is better, A or B?

A

Flow = what happens in brain during absorbing activity (e.g. playing sports, music)

Person in flow doesn't notice other activities

Time seems to pass quickly

Research – flow occurs due to chemical changes

B

- Flow is when someone is completely focused.
- This usually happens when you're doing something you like and can do well.
- Examples are playing an instrument, doing sports or doing something creative.
- When you're concentrating, you don't notice what else is happening around you.
- You might ignore noises or other people.
- Time will appear to pass by very quickly.
- The brain shows chemical changes during flow.

B Edit the rest of the notes about the article.

There are benefits to flow, which include increased attention, learning and developing skills.

They include better productivity, de-stressing, better creativity, motivation and happiness, too.

There are several characteristics of flow, but we do not need to experience them all at the same time.

They include:
- doing a rewarding activity
- having achievable goals
- feeling in control
- getting feedback straightaway
- having peace of mind.

Flow happens in many areas of life such as creative hobbies, sports, work and education.

There need to be clear goals, few distractions, some challenge and it must be enjoyable.

It is possible to practise flow by increasing the level of challenge and skill.

Lesson 6B

GRAMMAR | reported orders, requests and advice
VOCABULARY | reporting verbs
PRONUNCIATION | consonant clusters

VOCABULARY

reporting verbs

1 A Choose the correct word to complete the sentences.

1 My tutor **emphasised / suggested / threatened** I try some exercises in the mirror to help with my public speaking skills.
2 Juan **apologised / admitted / boasted** that he felt nervous about the presentation, so I offered to do it instead.
3 Police **questioned / boasted / persuaded** the suspect for several hours before letting her go.
4 Karen **claimed / threatened / refused** to lead the training session because she felt she didn't have the right skills.
5 Jenner **suggested / boasted / apologised** about having lots of friends online, but he's never even met half of them.
6 Ruth **claimed / boasted / questioned** that she had been very shy as a child, but I find that quite difficult to believe!

B Complete the article with the correct form of the verbs in brackets. Add *for* or *that* if necessary.

Are employee personality tests worth doing?

Martin Wilcox | Monday 3 September | 20.00 GMT

Have you ever done a personality test where you were asked lots of questions and had to choose the answer that was most like you? Sales Manager Sandie Frost tells us about the first test she took.

My employer [1] _____ (suggest) I take a personality test before I joined the company as Sales Manager. She [2] _____ (claim) it would give her – and me – a better idea of who I was and what kind of employee I would be. I'd refused [3] _____ (do) one earlier because I didn't think it would tell me anything I didn't already know. But this time I was curious.

I sat down at the computer and answered the questions. I found some of them to be unusual. For example, 'Do you often apologise for [4] _____ (do) something that you didn't do?' and, 'Have you ever [5] _____ (criticise) someone [6] _____ (being) late?'.

The results were interesting. My answers suggested that I was lacking a bit of confidence, but that I was an excellent team player – and all my previous bosses have praised me for working well with others!

PRONUNCIATION

2 A 🔊 **6.02** | **consonant clusters** | Listen and complete the sentences.

1 She _____ taking the money.
2 He _____ to leave the project.
3 They _____ me to move in with them.
4 He _____ that he didn't blame me.
5 She _____ that I apply for the role.

B Underline the groups of consonants in the reporting verbs.

C 🔊 **6.02** | Listen again and repeat.

GRAMMAR

reported orders, requests and advice

3 A The sentences below have a mistake. Choose the best option to correct the mistake.

1 'You should talk to someone about how you're feeling.' My wife advised me talk to someone about how I was feeling.
   a to talk   b to have talked   c talking
2 'Do you think you could organise a meeting for us next week?' She asked to organise a meeting for them for the following week.
   a I had to organise   b to me to organise
   c me to organise
3 'Can you help me find somewhere to live?' She asked whether I helped her to find somewhere to live.
   a I can help him   b I could help her
   c she could help me
4 'Don't run by the side of the pool!' He ordered we should run by the side of the pool.
   a we aren't   b we shouldn't   c us not to

B Complete the reported orders, requests and advice with the correct form of the verbs in brackets.

1 My line manager _____ (advise) me _____ (take) some management training sessions.
2 The teacher _____ (order) us _____ (stop) talking and get on with our work.
3 My boss _____ (ask) me _____ (rearrange) her schedule for the rest of the week.
4 She _____ (instruct) the children _____ (come) downstairs for dinner.
5 My colleague _____ (ask) me _____ (remind) him to send me the report.
6 I _____ (advise) my children _____ (not make) the same mistakes that I had in life.

40

6B

LISTENING

4 A 🔊 **6.03** | Listen to a conversation between two university students and answer the questions.

1 What explanation does the man give about ambiverts?
   a They make up the majority of people.
   b They frequently vary their behaviour.
   c They have a balance of characteristics.
2 What did the article say about ambiverts adapting to different situations?
   a It means they may find it difficult to make a decision.
   b It makes them suitable for a particular profession.
   c It can confuse other people in social settings.
3 What surprised the man about omnivert behaviour?
   a how they change their behaviour
   b how interested they are in different activities
   c how much rest they need after being with others
4 Why does the woman believe she's an omnivert?
   a She particularly enjoys going to a good party.
   b She finds that her feelings can change rapidly.
   c She shares her time between different groups.
5 What do the students agree about at the end?
   a The woman's personality type is very obvious.
   b No one is either fully extroverted or introverted.
   c It is difficult to determine the man's personality type.

B 🔊 **6.03** | Listen to the conversation again. Do the speakers present these ideas as facts (F) or opinions (O)?

1 An ambivert is someone whose behaviour is somewhere between introverted and extroverted.
2 There are more ambiverts than true extroverts or introverts.
3 Ambiverts are very successful as salespeople.
4 Omniverts can be extroverted or introverted depending on the day.
5 When omniverts have spent time on their own, they are keen to do something sociable.

C 🔊 **6.04** | Now listen to the final part of the discussion. How would the male speaker describe himself?

   a 'I understand when it's important to hear what others have to say, and when I should say something myself.'
   b 'I prefer to find out what other people's opinions are before I express my own.'
   c 'I can sometimes feel like I have little to contribute to a conversation, but at other times I'll feel more confident.'

D 📝 🔊 **6.05** | Listen to the recording and write what you hear. You will hear the sentence only once.

Lesson 6C

HOW TO ... | ask for advice and give advice tactfully
VOCABULARY | collocations with *get* and *take*
PRONUNCIATION | pitch for sounding tactful

VOCABULARY

collocations with *get* and *take*

1 A Complete the table with the words and phrases in the box.

> advice   involved   it personally   it wrong
> something off your chest   the message
> through to   your mind off

get	take

B Complete the forum posts with the correct form of a collocation with *take* or *get*.

Am I overreacting?

MandyB   Today at 3.19 p.m.

Hey everyone. I really need to ¹_____ my chest. So, the other day, I gave my friend a birthday present and when she opened it, all she said was, 'Oh!' and put it to one side – no thank you or anything! She hasn't seemed to ² _____ message that it upsets people if you don't say thanks. How can I say something to her without seeming childish?

Comments

JoJoB   Today at 3.23 p.m.

This makes me so mad! Try not to ³_____ personally, though. Maybe she was just distracted or something and you've got ⁴_____? If you really can't get over it, maybe just ask gently whether the gift was OK.

BeeZ   Today 3.27 p.m.

Hey, Mandy. Is there something you can do to ⁵_____ off what happened? If people don't have basic manners, you'll never ⁶_____ them by talking about it. ⁷_____ my advice and try to forget about it. Otherwise, other people might ⁸_____ involved, too, and you'll all end up in an argument over something that doesn't *really* matter.

How to ...

ask for advice and give advice tactfully

2 A 🔊 6.06 | Listen to three conversations. What problem is discussed in each one?

B 🔊 6.07 | Listen and complete the extracts.
1. Maybe I should just get a job instead. What _____?
2. Well, I hope _____, but have you been working hard enough?
3. _____ stick with it, but put a few more hours in.
4. Maybe I should look for a new job. What _____?
5. _____, I think you go to bed too late.
6. You _____ go to bed earlier.
7. Look, don't _____, but you're always in such a rush.
8. If _____, I'd get a little bowl to put your keys in.

PRONUNCIATION

3 A 🔊 6.08 | **pitch for sounding tactful** | Listen to the same advice given in two different ways. Which sounds more tactful (a or b)?
1. Perhaps you should do more preparation before your interview.
2. Have you thought about buying some new clothes?
3. It might be a good idea to think about how your words affect people.
4. Maybe you should just ask her what she thinks.

B 🔊 6.09 | Listen and repeat the tactful sentences.

SPEAKING

4 A 🔊 6.10 | Complete the conversation with one word in each gap. Then listen and check.

Mark: Do you think I ¹_____ buy this baseball cap?
Rob: Don't ²_____ me wrong, but I think you might be a little old for baseball caps now ...
Mark: Really?! So what ³_____ you get?
Rob: If you really ⁴_____ my advice, it's not a hat you should be worrying about ...
Mark: What? What do you mean?
Rob: Well, you do dress a bit like a teenager. Maybe it's time to buy more grown-up clothes?
Mark: Hmm ... it ⁵_____ be a good idea to get a couple of shirts I suppose.
Rob: Yeah, that would be a good start. Why ⁶_____ you ask the sales assistant for advice?
Mark: Good idea. Excuse me ... !

B 🔊 6.11 | You are Rob in Ex 4A. Listen and speak after the beep. Record yourself if you can.

C Listen to your recording and compare it to Ex 4A.

Lesson 6D

VOCABULARY | fillers
READING | the science of lying

VOCABULARY

fillers

1 A 🔊 **6.12** | Listen and complete the sentences.
1 I really don't know what to do about finding a new job. ...., how are you?
2 ...., I told her that I wouldn't be going back to that café any time soon!
3 ...., I don't really like that kind of food, so why she'd made it when I'd told her that, I don't know.
4 I find TV so boring these days. ...., I did watch a good film last night.
5 ...., let's get started. ...., in front of you, you'll see several scientific instruments.

B Put the sentences in the correct order to complete the anecdote.
a Well, I'll never try and use my phone whilst cycling again – that's for sure!
b I've always hated loud noises, so it really freaked me out. Anyway, I looked around and guess what I saw?
c So, I ran over to help the cyclist up and guess what? He was completely fine. Apparently, he'd been looking at his phone.
d So, I was on my way to meet a friend, when suddenly I heard a huge bang behind me.
e A bicycle had crashed into the wall behind me! As I say, I hate loud noises, so I was pretty shaken up.

READING

2 A Complete the article with the subheadings (a–g). There are three subheadings that you do not need.
a When does lying start?
b What are the consequences of a lie?
c How does lying affect us?
d The history of lying.
e Why do we lie?
f What is a lie?
g How lying can be beneficial.

B Read the article again. Are the statements True (T), False (F) or Not Mentioned (NM)?
1 You take part in a lie if you pretend to believe it.
2 Not saying something can still be described as a lie.
3 People believe there are 'good' lies and 'bad' lies.
4 Certain people are more likely to lie than others.
5 Our lies become more complicated the older we get.
6 Criminals are most likely to tell the biggest lies.
7 Lying is relatively easy for our brains to do.
8 Adults are less likely to lie if they were punished for doing so as a child.

The science of lying

**We all lie occasionally lie,
but what is the science behind it all?**

Rachel Humphreys | Friday 21 July | 15.59 GMT

1 ....

Scientists classify lies in three ways: they are either completely deceitful, half-truths or omissions (when something is left out of a story to give a particular impression).

2 ....

Scientists have identified two reasons for lying: either the liar thinks they will gain more from lying than being honest, or they aren't really sure what the truth is. Non-scientists tend to think of lies in terms of how serious they are. This ranges from socially-beneficial white lies where, for example, we tell someone we like their outfit even though we don't, to more serious 'antisocial' lies, such as denying involvement in a crime.

3 ....

Psychologists confirm that children tell lies from around the age of two. Some believe this is an important step in a child's development. In order to tell a lie, you need to be able to consider the effect it will have on another person and plan the lie in order to get the desired result. Most of us grow out of this tendency as we understand more about what is considered moral and we are better able to regulate our thoughts and actions.

4 ....

Lying is a complex process that requires effort for our brains. Research indicates that the more one lies, the less challenging it becomes to lie, and the more likely one is to do it again. Scientists don't know why we don't all lie more often to get what we want, but they believe it is because we learn that it is socially unacceptable. If lying isn't punished at an early age, there's a higher probability that a child will grow up to become a dishonest adult – with poor consequences for society as a whole.

5-6 REVIEW

GRAMMAR

1 Complete the sentences using the past perfect or past perfect continuous form of the verbs in brackets.

1. Clara was exhausted because she _____ (rush) around all morning.
2. I was looking forward to the trip because I _____ (never / go) to Spain before.
3. It was very wet outside because it _____ (rain) all night.
4. She _____ (live) with her parents whilst she was looking for a new job.
5. Archie _____ (already / see) the film twice, but was happy to go again.
6. They _____ (know) each other for a long time, but had never been particularly close.

2 Complete the forum posts using the correct form of the verb in brackets.

CareerSeeker advice forum

AliceK — 1 day ago
I had always dreamed of being a social media influencer, getting paid to go to amazing places or test beauty products and so on, and ¹_____ (plan) to study Social Media Marketing to help me get there. But I've changed my mind. I was only going to ²_____ (take) the course because it sounded cool. I was supposed to ³_____ (finish) my university applications at the weekend but didn't. I wouldn't mind a career in writing but have no idea how to go about it. Please help!

CrazyCat — 18 hours ago
I was expecting ⁴_____ (get) onto an ecology study programme and I ⁵_____ (mean) to be starting next week. But unfortunately, I didn't get the grades 😞. I ⁶_____ (hope) it would lead to a role in government, so I could play my part in fighting climate change but I guess that's not going to happen. What should I do now?

ZaC — 7 hours ago
I was already considering ⁷_____ (become) a fashion designer and then I found out about sustainable fashion design and that appealed to me even more. I was thinking of ⁸_____ (go) to university but I don't know which course to go for. Any ideas?

3 Choose the correct word to complete the sentences.

1. I walked home in the dark, _____ wasn't as scary as I expected.
   a which   b where   c when
2. I get advice about my work from my friend Amy, _____ is a brilliant editor.
   a whose   b which   c who
3. We travelled around the Greek islands, _____ was a great experience.
   a where   b when   c which
4. That's my friend Maddie, _____ photography is truly amazing.
   a which   b who   c whose
5. We should go in Spring, _____ it's nice and quiet.
   a where   b when   c which

4 Complete the article with the correct form of the words in brackets.

Worst birthday ever!

Monday 12 July | 16.43 GMT

Lots of you have been waiting for me to upload photos of my birthday party at the weekend. Well, it never happened!

We headed down to the pool but it was closed because it ¹_____ (need / clean). We ²_____ (not be / allow) to sit on the grass in the sun. So, we decided to go to the lake for a swim instead. But there was a new sign up – swimming ³_____ no longer _____ (permit) there. I think it's because there's some pollution there at the moment. Since it ⁴_____ (be / forbid) to swim in the river because of the strong current, we gave up on the whole idea, and decided to go for something to eat.

Guess what?! We ⁵_____ (not can / eat) at my favourite café without a reservation, so we ⁶_____ (have to) go somewhere else. The food was great, though, so that saved the day!

5 Report the orders, requests and advice with the verbs in brackets.

1. 'Sit down and be quiet!', shouted the teacher.
   The teacher _____ (order) and be quiet.
2. 'You should ask the chemist for some eye drops', said Mum.
   Mum _____ (advise) some eyedrops.
3. 'Could you pass me that magazine, please?' said Helena.
   Helena _____ (ask) the magazine.
4. 'Turn the laptop off when you've finished with it,' said Grandad.
   Grandad _____ (tell) with it.
5. 'I'd like some further information from you,' said the course admissions secretary.
   The course admissions secretary _____ (request) from us.

REVIEW 5–6

VOCABULARY

6 Complete the sentences with the phrases in the box.

> by the time   for ages   for a while   in no time
> just moments earlier   up to that point

1 The house was in complete darkness _____ I got home and everyone was in bed.
2 The lecture had been fascinating _____, but I lost interest when it changed topic.
3 The tree crashed onto the road we'd been on _____. We had a lucky escape!
4 I've been waiting here _____! Where have you been?
5 Stop bothering me! Go and play over there _____ so I can finish this.
6 'I'll have the room painted _____!', said Josep optimistically.

7 Choose the correct word or phrase to complete the sentences.

1 I've always enjoyed writing, so I'd like to go into **accountancy / journalism / agriculture** after uni.
2 My cousin went into **banking / social work / medicine** after completing a degree in finance.
3 I'd love to work in **publishing / construction / research**. I like the idea of editing books.
4 My dad was an accountant for years, then **started out / reinvented / switched** himself as a carpenter.
5 Our **research / part-time / entrepreneur** team studies new developments in the medical field.
6 I'd love to **advance / start out / set up** my own beauty company one day.

8 Complete the conversations with the words in the box.

> delay   frozen   get into   host   link   on mute

1 A: Hi, Fatima. Can you hear me?
B: Hello! I can see you but not hear you! I think you must be ¹_____!
A: Oh, yes. Can you hear me now?
B: I can hear you, but your screen's ²_____, so you're stuck in the same position.
A: Oh, ha ha! Hang on, I think Noah's trying to ³_____ the meeting. Oh, it says that you're the ⁴_____, not me.
B: Yes – I'll let him in. Hi, Noah!

2 A: There seems to be some kind of ⁵_____ and we keep speaking over each other.
B: I'm going to log out and back in again. Can you re-send the ⁶_____ for the meeting?
A: Sure – I'll do it now.

9 Complete the words with the prefixes in the box.

> dis   im   mis   re   sub   un

1 I'm a very _____patient person and want everything to happen when I need it to!
2 I think I must have _____read the advert when I applied for the job. I thought the salary was higher.
3 As well as the title, you need to think of a great _____heading to get people to read an article.
4 I think there have been some _____honest reviews about the restaurant's service.
5 Can you _____do this document, please? There are a lot of spelling mistakes in it.
6 Try not to have _____realistic expectations when it comes to securing your first job.

10 Choose the correct reporting verbs to complete the sentences.

1 Hanna **denied / apologised** being an internet troll.
2 He **regretted / insisted** on driving her to the station.
3 Can you **remind / accept** me to invite Alex on Saturday?
4 Rob's just been arrested. They've **accused / insisted** him of fraud!
5 I'd like to **accept / apologise** if I have misled you in any way.
6 He **refused / denied** to move his car, even though I asked him politely.

11 Complete the sentences with the correct form of *take* or *get*.

1 Can we have a quick chat? I need to _____ something off my chest.
2 Please don't _____ it personally, but it looks like you haven't cleaned your shoes for months!
3 I think I _____ it wrong about Iwona being unfriendly. She's actually really nice.
4 Has going for a walk _____ your mind off things? I hope you feel better now.
5 No matter how many times I ask him to close the door, he just doesn't _____ the message!
6 You're great at giving people advice, but you aren't so good at _____ it.
7 Sorry, I don't want to _____ involved in your argument. It's between you and Beth.
8 I can't seem to _____ through to Olivia about the importance of doing homework.

12 Number the lines of the conversation in the correct order.

a So, when will you find out?
b Right. And what will you do if you don't get the place?
c I'm not sure. Hopefully before the end of this month.
d OK. Let's go and watch TV for a bit instead then.
e I'll probably go into teaching instead. Anyway, let's not talk about that! It makes me nervous.
f Are you still planning on becoming an educational psychologist?
g Well, it depends if I get accepted onto the postgraduate course.

Lesson 7A

GRAMMAR | past modals of deduction
VOCABULARY | compound adjectives; chance
PRONUNCIATION | connected speech: past modals of deduction

VOCABULARY

compound adjectives

1 Complete the online profile with the words in the box. You may need to use the words more than once.

> changing consuming famous hand
> lasting respected year-old

Former dance school student reaches new heights

Janie Hansen is a twenty-four-¹_____ ballet dancer from the UK. She is a widely ²_____ dancer at the London Ballet, where she is on track to become prima ballerina. She is hoping to follow in the footsteps of her mother – the world-³_____ dancer, Imelda Khrushcheva. Dancing careers are often short-lived in comparison with other professions, but Imelda's long-⁴_____ career is what inspired Janie to take up ballet herself.

Janie started dancing at the age of ten, wearing second-⁵_____ shoes. Ballet quickly became an all-⁶_____ passion for her. Once she had reached the age of fourteen, she knew she wanted to dance professionally, and auditioned to join a leading ballet school.

This was a life-⁷_____ decision. Serious ballet training is especially time-⁸_____, and she spent several hours a day in dance classes alongside her ordinary education. Her efforts eventually paid off: she is in her second season as a soloist with the London Ballet, and she looks set to rise to stardom like her mother.

chance

2 Choose the correct word to complete the sentences.

1. Participants were selected at _____ and asked to complete a series of tasks.
   a fortunate   b random   c chance
2. I went into acting quite _____ when someone gave me a free lesson as a gift.
   a by chance   b accidental   c unfortunate
3. In a _____ accident at the theatre, the scenery collapsed, but no one was seriously injured.
   a chance   b fortunate   c freak
4. Only a _____ few ever become superstars in the film industry.
   a fortunate   b freak   c chance
5. She kicked me during the football match, but I think it was _____.
   a chance   b accidental   c fortunate

GRAMMAR

past modals of deduction

3 A The sentences below have a mistake. Choose the best option to correct the mistake.

1. She <u>may</u> have been affected by the fall – I guess that's why she doesn't ride now.
   a can   b must   c can't
2. I <u>can't</u> have left my purse on the train – it isn't in my bag!
   a must   b must not   c can
3. You <u>might</u> have seen Małgorzata in town because she's away on holiday at the moment.
   a must   b could   c can't
4. They <u>must have</u> stopped the match because of the snow, but I'm not sure.
   a may have   b can't have   c must have been

B Complete the article with the correct form of the verbs in brackets and a modal of deduction.

The world's top table-tennis town

Michael Cabo | Monday 19 Feb | 16:18 GMT

We all admire those who've dedicated themselves to becoming a top athlete or classical musician, but a study of top performers has shown that they ¹_____ (got) there if they hadn't had the right circumstances.

In the 1980s, Silverdale Road in Reading, UK, produced several first-class table-tennis players. You would be right in thinking that this ²_____ (happen) by chance. It sounds virtually impossible for a dozen top players to have come from a single street, so coincidence simply ³_____ (have) anything to do with it. How, then, did Silverdale Road produce so many brilliant players?

At the time, the young people's school teacher was the nation's top table-tennis coach and he gave every child in the school a table-tennis try-out. If they showed talent, he trained them. It ⁴_____ (be) very exciting to work with such an inspiring coach! What's more, the youngsters had access to a 24-hour table-tennis club for practice. Not many young people at the time ⁵_____ possibly _____ (have) such an opportunity.

Of course, those who did become champions ⁶_____ (be) sitting around at home all day: they also put in the time and effort that ultimately paid off and this ⁷_____ (make) their teacher very proud!

7A

PRONUNCIATION

4 A 🔊 **7.01 | connected speech: past modals of deduction |** Listen and complete the sentences.

1 You .... been living here that long, surely!
2 Meiko .... known the questions in advance.
3 I .... done the amount of training required anyway.
4 It .... been cold with the roof off like that.
5 They .... eaten before they came.

B 🔊 **7.01 |** Listen again and repeat.

READING

5 A Read the article. Which three reasons are given for people suddenly developing impressive abilities?

B Complete the article with the missing sentences (a–g). There is one sentence that you don't need.

a However, this is extremely rare.
b A study of one group showed that they had become very good artists.
c The closest a person might get to being truly great at something is to put in a lot of hours for their chosen specialism.
d They are simply unable to explain how this came about.
e In a healthy brain, the left-hand side tends to limit the right.
f A small number of autistic people appear to have incredible skills that the rest of us can only dream of.
g This might occur in a freak accident or through illness, accidental damage or a medical complication.

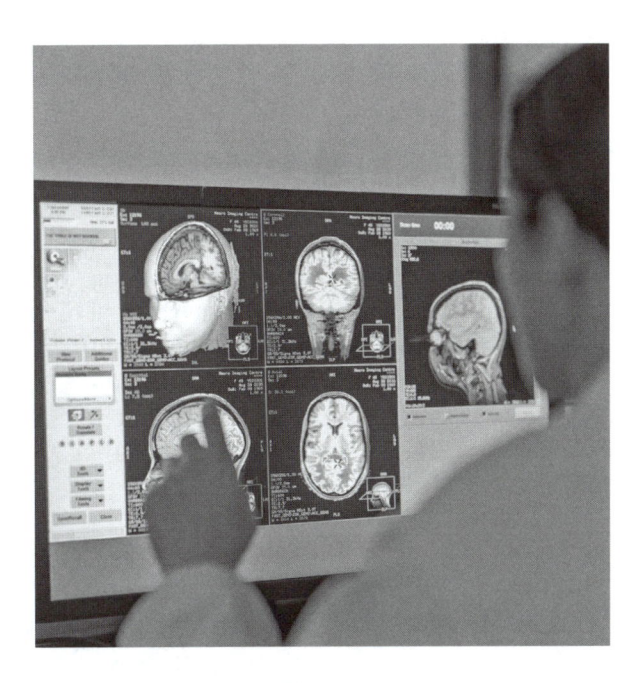

How do some people become sudden geniuses?

Like Tony Cicoria and Jon Sarkin, who developed sudden interests and impressive abilities after a brain injury, there have been others who have found themselves in possession of an incredible skill after suffering damage to the brain. Emma Cardigan investigates the science behind this fascinating phenomenon.

Research shows that the most common way for people to suddenly develop impressive abilities is via a brain injury. [1] .... As a consequence of such traumas, serotonin (a chemical which affects mood) leaks out of dying brain cells into the brain around them. This creates new connections in the brain which appear to make people more creative.

Other research has looked at people with certain kinds of life-changing dementia. They became increasingly creative as their brain was more and more affected by the disease. [2] .... This is particularly interesting when the same people had shown no or little interest in the subject earlier in their lives. In some cases, the further the illness progressed, the better the patients' skills became.

When the patients' brains were scanned, researchers realised that the left-hand side of the brain (which controls logic and language) was more affected by dementia than the right (which is responsible for creativity). [3] .... This is because usually, being logical is more of an advantage to us in terms of decision-making and general life tasks. In a person with dementia, the right-hand side of the brain becomes free to be as creative as it likes. So, this indicates that when the left side of the brain is damaged, some people may suddenly become creative geniuses. [4] .... The vast majority of dementia sufferers do not acquire new skills.

But what about 'ordinary' geniuses who have not suffered brain injury? [5] .... This is true of forty-two-year-old Daniel Tammet, who, amongst other things, can do fantastic mathematical calculations impressively quickly. People like Tammet have what is known as 'savant syndrome'. One theory suggests that as savants' brains are developing during childhood, the left-hand side had extremely low levels of serotonin, which allowed the right-hand side to become more active. In the case of sudden savants, like Sarkin, they also feel a desire to work hard at their new talent, which makes them even better at it.

As for those who have not suffered a brain injury, it's simply not possible to *become* a genius, or certainly not suddenly. [6] .... In fact, experts say we need to do at least 10,000 hours of 'purposeful practice' (i.e. trying to do something better each and every time we try it) to become an expert. Even then, true genius is far out of reach for most of us.

Lesson 7B

GRAMMAR | *wish, if only, should have*
VOCABULARY | idioms: regrets
PRONUNCIATION | chunking in idioms

VOCABULARY

idioms: regrets

1 A Match the idioms in the box with the descriptions (1–6).

> a blessing in disguise   back to the drawing board
> a piece of cake   miss the boat
> not be someone's cup of tea
> the grass is always greener on the other side

1 'Oh, that exam was so much more straightforward than I expected. I bet I get 100 percent.'
2 'I'm sorry, the auditions for the play took place yesterday.'
3 'I missed the audition but it's turned out for the best because I've been offered something better.'
4 'I made the switch from opera to classical singing, but it's not as much fun.'
5 'I think I need to re-consider my career options. Acting hasn't worked out for me.'
6 'I'm not going to see a musical again – that was awful!'

B Choose the correct word to complete the sentences.

1 **A:** How's it going with your band?
   B: Our singer left to join another band. He thought the grass was _____ on the other side.
   a better   **b** greener   **c** whiter

2 **A:** Hey! How was your exam?
   B: It was a piece of _____ – I actually finished half an hour early!
   a cake   **b** bread   **c** pie

3 **A:** I've missed the _____ – I should've kept an eye on when the deadline was.
   B: There'll be other jobs to go for, don't worry.
   a boat   **b** bus   **c** timetable

4 **A:** Fancy coming to see the play tonight?
   B: No, it's not my cup of _____.
   a tea   **b** water   **c** coffee

5 **A:** Did you do the swimming competition?
   B: No. But it was a blessing in _____ because I had a rest and now I'm making great progress.
   a a suit   **b** clothes   **c** disguise

6 **A:** Why are you deleting your work?
   B: I've decided to go back to the _____ board. It just wasn't good enough.
   a notice   **b** drawing   **c** white

PRONUNCIATION

2 A 🔊 7.02 | chunking in idioms | Listen and complete the sentences.

1 I always found driving _____, right from my first lesson.
2 Missing the concert was _____ – I had an early night instead.
3 Icelandic death metal _____, I'm afraid!
4 _____ – I can tell you that for sure.
5 The funding fell through, so I had to _____.
6 Sandra _____ because she didn't apply in time.

B 🔊 7.02 | Listen again and repeat the sentences. Remember to say the idioms as chunks.

GRAMMAR

wish, if only, should have

3 A Choose the correct word or phrase to complete the sentences.

1 I wish **I had** / **I'd had** / **I have** more to eat this lunchtime. I'm hungry again already.
2 If only **we lived** / **we live** / **we'd lived** nearer the city – we'd be able to go shopping more.
3 You **shouldn't only have** / **shouldn't have** / **should have** told me about the party. I'd have gone.
4 I wish you **will** / **do** / **would** stop talking while my favourite programme's on!
5 If only **I had** / **I hadn't** / **I'd have** brought my guitar with me. I need to practise for the gig.
6 I **should have** / **shouldn't have** / **wouldn't have** let you down. I'm sorry.

B Complete the article about regrets with the correct form of the verbs in brackets.

> 'It's better to regret the things you have done than the things you haven't.' That's what they say. But is there any truth to the matter?
>
> Compare the following: 'I wish I ¹_____ (not try) to climb Mount Everest and fulfil a dream,' and 'If only I ²_____ (work) harder at school, I ³_____ (have) a better job now.' Which of these are you more likely to hear? The second, because there's nothing you can do about it now. On the other hand, even if you'd failed to reach the top of Everest, at least you'd have given it a go.
>
> However, we do regret some things that we've done. Think about these situations: 'I shouldn't ⁴_____ (speak) to my friend like that', 'If only I ⁵_____ (not crash) the car', 'I wish I ⁶_____ (not eat) so much food. These definitely aren't the same as climbing Everest.
>
> Perhaps the old saying isn't as wise as it sounds!

LISTENING

4 A 🔊 **7.03** | Listen to three people talking about regret. Match the speakers (1–3) with their regrets (a–c).

  a I regret not knowing about something I could have done as a job.
  b I regret not pursuing an academic subject I was good at.
  c I regret not taking a risk with an uncertain career.

B 🔊 **7.03** | Listen again and put the events into the correct order for each speaker.

Speaker 1
  a taking qualifications
  b learning something few other people did at the time
  c making a decision

Speaker 2
  a enjoying something very much
  b rejecting a particular route
  c being creative

Speaker 3
  a feeling relatively satisfied with a decision
  b opting for a particular course of study
  c being unaware that something was an option

WRITING

a personal essay

5 A Read the title of the article. What information do you think the article might include?
  a a regretted decision
  b an unexpected realisation
  c a new course of action

B Skim the article quickly and check.

C Read the article again and match the topics (a–f) with the paragraphs (1–6).
  a the main event
  b the theme of the article
  c a summary
  d more details about the main event
  e a consequence
  f a good decision was made

D Plan an article of your own with one of the following titles.
  • The grass is greener on the other side
  • The grass isn't greener on the other side

  1 Think about an event that has led to you thinking that the grass is/isn't greener on the other side (use your imagination if you prefer).
  2 Use the paragraph plan in Ex 5C and the model answer. Think about what information you will include in each paragraph.

E Write your article using your notes. Write at least 140 words.

The grass is sometimes greener on the other side

[1] People who spend a lot of time scrolling through other people's online profiles (myself included) often can't help comparing their own lives with those of the people they're following.

[2] We usually compare ourselves negatively: 'He's got a better job than I have', 'She has a better social life than me', and so on. It's easy to feel that the grass is greener on the other side, but most of the time it isn't: it's just people's desire to show off that leads them to post only the positive aspects of their lives.

[3] I've fallen into this trap myself. I used to spend hours looking at what people were doing and feeling fed up of my own life. I didn't consider the things I had that *they* might envy, such as *my* job, or my close relationship with my family.

[4] Then one day, I suddenly thought, maybe I can use this information to make positive changes in my own life! 'I must be able to improve my own career', I thought. 'Why don't I look harder for budget holidays? Maybe I should join that sports club I've been thinking about for so long.'

[5] So, I did just that. I gained an extra qualification that helped me get promoted. I went backpacking round my country; and I joined the sports club and made new friends!

[6] Although it's tempting to see other people's successes as your failures, there's always time to make positive changes in your own life.

Lesson 7C

HOW TO ... | describe a process
VOCABULARY | phrasal verbs: explaining
PRONUNCIATION | stress in phrasal verbs

VOCABULARY

phrasal verbs: explaining

1 A Complete the sentences with the words in the box.

> across   down (×2)   into   out (×2)   over   through

1 Have you got time to go .... what we need to include in our essay, please?
2 Your speech was great, but don't forget to slow .... so you don't sound rushed.
3 I can't figure .... what my boss wants me to do. I'll have to ask her to explain.
4 I deal with big projects by breaking them .... into smaller tasks.
5 You don't need to go .... all the details – just tell me the results.
6 I sometimes find it difficult to get my message .... in meetings and no one listens.
7 If you need someone to talk .... your problems with, I'm a great listener.
8 Caro left .... some referencing in her assignment and got a low grade because of it.

B Choose the correct word to complete the sentences.

1 When you speak to the police, it's important not to .... out any information.
   a break   **b** figure   **c** leave
2 I need to figure .... some safety rules before I go on the climbing wall.
   a out   **b** over   **c** down
3 Steph went .... every minor detail. It was so boring!
   a into   **b** across   **c** down
4 You've got your .... across clearly.
   a talk   **b** thing   **c** point
5 Have you got anyone you can talk things .... with?
   a into   **b** through   **c** down
6 Please slow ....! I can't understand you.
   a out   **b** down   **c** into

PRONUNCIATION

2 🔊 **7.04** | **stress in phrasal verbs** | Underline the stressed part of the phrasal verbs in bold. Then listen and check.

1 There's no point in **going over** the whole story again.
2 You need to **figure out** what you want to do in life.
3 Remember to **slow down** when you're speaking so people can understand you.
4 Please don't **go into** all the details of what happened now – you can tell me later.
5 I **left out** some critical information in my interview.

How to ...

describe a process

3 A 🔊 **7.05** | Listen to an explainer video. Who is the speaker? What process is she describing?

B 🔊 **7.06** | Listen to the rest of the video and number the stages in the correct order.
   a Include relevant references.
   b Check the order of required information.
   c Provide contact information.
   d Check your work for errors.
   e List your work experience and qualifications.
   f Add a professional-looking photo.

C 🔊 **7.06** | Listen again and complete the extracts.
1 ...., you need to look at the platform where your profile will appear.
2 The first thing you might be asked to do is upload a current photo. ...., but …
3 .... use a photo showing you in a social setting.
4 .... organising your qualifications.
5 .... checking through what you've written.

SPEAKING

4 A 🔊 **7.07** | Complete the conversation with one word in each gap. Then listen and check.

Jo: So, what are you going to do this summer?
Tom: Well, I'd love to plan a walking trip like you did. But I've got no idea how to get started!
Jo: Well, to [1] .... with, you'll need to decide where you're going!
Tom: Ha ha! True. Well, I'd like to go to the mountains, but I guess that means having to camp.
Jo: You can [2] .... you want. Or you could stay in a hostel near where you're walking.
Tom: OK, and [3] .... I've found somewhere, can I just turn up or do I need to book in advance?
Jo: Well, I'd [4] .... just turning up because they might not have any rooms left.
Tom: OK. Any other advice?
Jo: It's [5] .... that you tell someone where you're going each day and when you'll be back.
Tom: What, in case I get lost? But I'll have my phone.
Jo: Yeah, but you might not get a signal in the mountains. I'd [6] .... buying an actual map and compass, too.
Tom: Good idea. Thanks for the advice!

B 🔊 **7.08** | You are Jo in Ex 4A. Listen and speak after the beep. Record yourself if you can.

C Listen to your recording and compare it to 4A.

Speak anywhere   Go to the interactive speaking practice

Lesson 7D

GRAMMAR | adverbials of concession
LISTENING | an interview about talents

GRAMMAR

adverbials of concession

1 A Choose the correct word or phrase to complete the sentences.

1 I've always loved chess. **Although / However / On the one hand**, I'm not good at it.
2 It's important to nurture talent. Don't push people hard, **although / on the one hand / though**.
3 On the **other / although / one** hand, I'd like to be self-employed. On the other, I like the security of a full-time job.
4 **However / Though / On the other hand** Amy showed early talent, she hasn't progressed much.
5 I studied art at university, **though / on the one hand / however** I don't do much painting now.
6 Arlo loves football. He's not the best player, **on the other hand / although / however**.

B Complete the article with the adverbs in the box. You need to use some of them more than once.

> although   however   on the one hand
> on the other hand   though

Why young talents don't always reach their potential

There are several reasons why someone might not achieve their full potential, ¹_____ they might have done very well as a child in school. You may know of someone who was the best football player in school by far. ²_____, they didn't become a top sportsperson like everyone expected them to. Perhaps they reached a 'plateau': a point at which they never actually got any better. ³_____, they may just have got bored, stopped trying or even got as far as they were physically capable of.

But what about those who really could succeed but don't? ⁴_____ many children are encouraged by teachers to develop skills, once they move to another school or leave education, it may be difficult for them to find the support they need. ⁵_____, this is often down to a lack of funding, but ⁶_____, it could be that formal training is simply not available.

LISTENING

2 A 🔊 7.09 | Listen to a radio interview about talent and choose the correct answer (a–c).

1 Why does Michael no longer play the violin?
  a He has achieved everything he wanted to.
  b He hopes to pursue another activity he likes.
  c He has become fed up with the pressure.
2 What does Michael say when asked if he'd always wanted to play the violin?
  a He realised he was good at it from an early age.
  b He started playing because of someone else.
  c He hoped his playing would support his family.
3 What is Michael's opinion on parents encouraging their children?
  a They shouldn't push them too hard.
  b They shouldn't worry if they don't always do well.
  c They shouldn't try to fulfil their own dreams.
4 How do Michael's parents feel about him giving up?
  a pleased that he has found something else to do
  b surprised that he feels the way he does
  c disappointed that he won't play anymore
5 What does Michael say about future regret?
  a He thinks it is unlikely.
  b He thinks he might return to the violin.
  c He says it depends on his cricket career.
6 How might Michael feel if he isn't successful at cricket?
  a proud of giving it a go
  b eager to try out another idea
  c confident he'll do well at something else

B Are the statements True (T) or False (F)?

1 Michael believes he will succeed at cricket.
2 His parents were not wealthy.
3 He does not understand why his parents wanted him to play the violin.
4 His parents are unhappy about him playing cricket.
5 He says that he often regrets things he hasn't done.
6 He won't be too upset if he doesn't become a cricket player.

C 🔊 7.09 | Listen again and check.

Lesson 8A

GRAMMAR | participle clauses
VOCABULARY | collocations with *go*, *have* and *make*; describing homes and living conditions
PRONUNCIATION | pitch in participle clauses

VOCABULARY

collocations with *go*, *have* and *make*

1 Complete the sentences with the correct form of *go*, *have* or *make*.
   1 Something's .... wrong with the boiler. Would you mind taking a look?
   2 I might .... a go at repainting this room at the weekend.
   3 Here, you take a look. I can't .... sense of these instructions at all!
   4 Many young people don't .... the opportunity to buy a house until their mid-thirties.
   5 Moving the furniture around has .... such a difference to this room.
   6 Unfortunately, buying a home often .... hand in hand with getting into debt.

describing homes and living conditions

2 Choose the correct word to complete the advert.

Massey's Estates

Well-maintained studio flat in city centre

- In excellent ¹**condition / fashionable / character**
- Very ²**elegant / spacious / condition** for this kind of property (45m²)
- Separate kitchen and bathroom decorated in a ³**character / fashionable / secure** manner
- Comes fully furnished with ⁴**spacious / secure / stylish** decoration.

Four bedroom detached property

- Nineteenth-century house with plenty of ⁵**elegant / condition / character**, including large windows
- Extremely ⁶**elegant / exclusive / secure** staircase leading to upper floors
- Price on application

GRAMMAR

participle clauses

3A Choose the correct word or phrase to complete the sentences.
   1 **Have worked / Having worked / Working** hard all week, Beth was really looking forward to the weekend.
   2 **Finishing / Having finished / Finish** repainting her bedroom, Nisha decided she didn't really like the colour.
   3 **Sat / Sitting / Having sat** in her living room, Natalia had a beautiful view of the river.
   4 **Not having completed / Completing / Not completing** the repairs to his roof, Dan was alarmed to see heavy rain forecast that weekend.
   5 **Opening / Having opened / Opened** the cupboards, Mike had to put his hands up to stop a pile of old boxes falling on his head.

B Complete the sentences using the correct participle clause of the verbs in brackets.
   1 .... (clean) the windows, Jo stood back and admired her work.
   2 .... (finish) the assignment, Chloe emailed it to her tutor and sighed with relief.
   3 .... (panic), Karl searched his pockets rapidly, worried he had lost his car keys.
   4 .... (promise) she'd make an appearance, Fatima arrived early for the party.
   5 .... (leave) his car in a well-lit street, Al was surprised to find his window broken on his return.

PRONUNCIATION

4A 🔊 8.01 | **pitch in participle clauses** | Listen and underline the clauses which have a higher pitch than the rest of the sentence.
   1 Having rented throughout his 30s, David was finally able to buy his own home.
   2 Looking out of the window, Sasha realised how much she loved this place.
   3 Having worked at the company for 50 years, she finally retired last month.
   4 Thinking about their future, the couple started researching schools in the area.
   5 Having lived in many different places, Kim finally decided to settle down.

B 🔊 8.01 | Listen again and repeat.

READING

5 A Read the article. Which topic is NOT mentioned?

> commuting   cost of living   jobs   local transport
> mental health   nightlife   pollution

B Read the article again. What arguments are made for and against moving to the countryside? Make notes.

Why young people are moving to the country

For many young people growing up in the countryside, life in the big city has lots of obvious attractions – more opportunities, better nightlife, a bus service that runs more than once an hour – the list is endless. So, it's easy to see why so many of them leave their rural upbringings behind. However, recently more young people are settling outside of major cities. So, what's prompted the change?

For many, the main reasons are financial. 'We just couldn't afford to live there anymore. We were living in a two-bedroom flat, with no garden, nowhere near the city centre, and most of our salaries were going on rent and bills.'. This is Lucie Darvell – a young professional who, recently moved from a flat in London to a cottage in Sussex. For her, it's more cost-effective to live in the countryside. 'You just get more for your money. Here we get three bedrooms – one of which I use as an office – a garden, a parking space outside … it just makes more sense.'

Others like Lucie have also said the move has had a positive impact on their mental health. 'In Manchester, I felt stressed all the time. I lived in a small flat, didn't have much money and was surrounded by grey buildings, traffic and pollution.' says India West – a financial analyst originally from Bolton. 'Out here, I've got nature right on my doorstep. There's a forest five minutes' walk in one direction, a beautiful river ten minutes the other way – it's just much easier to relax here.'

However, the majority of people who have made the transition still have to commute into the city, which has its own disadvantages. 'All that money I've saved on rent now goes on my train ticket.' says media producer, Tom Carter. 'And the journey's not that great either. It should take an hour door to door, but with all the delays, it can sometimes take me two hours to get to work.'

Some have also found it all a bit quiet in the countryside. 'There's also just not as much going on out here.' says Tom's partner Alex. 'I miss being able to go to galleries and nice restaurants.

So, for many, the countryside provides a welcome escape from the stresses of everyday life. For others, it's a change of pace they're not quite ready for. However, if the cost of living continues to rise, we may well see more and more young people ditching their expensive coffees for a pair of wellies.

WRITING

an application letter/email

6 A Read the extract from an application letter. What kind of company is the writer applying to?

> I would like to apply for the role of .... as advertised on the Inspire website on Monday 3rd July.
>
> I have experience in a similar position, having worked for Blackwell's Agency for twelve months. I am experienced in keeping the company website up-to-date with details, and showing clients around properties. I would now like to take the next step and become a sales negotiator.
>
> I believe I would be suited to this role because I have excellent communication skills, a friendly and confident attitude and good knowledge of the local market.

B Read the letter again and underline the formal phrases.

C Read the job advertisement and make notes on why you would be suited to this position. You can invent skills and abilities if necessary.

Trainee Sales Negotiator

Landley's Estate Agency

Posted 3 days ago   **Apply**

An excellent opportunity to join our sales team as a trainee sales negotiator with on-the-job training.

Duties will include:
- interviewing clients to identify needs
- contacting clients regularly to advise them of suitable properties and to arrange viewings
- negotiating with potential purchasers
- achieving sales targets as agreed with the Branch Manager

You will need:
Excellent customer service skills
Teamwork skills
A high level of professionalism
Sales experience an advantage

D Now write a formal letter of application for the post, using the advert and your notes in Ex 6C. Write at least 140 words.

Lesson 8B

GRAMMAR | conditionals with conjunctions
VOCABULARY | world issues
PRONUNCIATION | stress in conditional sentences

VOCABULARY

world issues

1 A Match the words in the box with the descriptions (1–10).

> civil rights   endangered languages   global warming
> homelessness   housing   justice   literacy
> overcrowding   poverty   unemployment

1 The group has been sleeping in an abandoned building for the past two years. ....
2 My grandmother speaks Bathari, which is rapidly dying out. ....
3 After decades of court appearances, he was finally found guilty and sentenced to twenty-five years in prison. ....
4 This area of Hong Kong is one of the most densely populated places in the world. ....
5 All citizens should have political and social freedom, and equality. ....
6 Rising temperatures are causing more frequent extreme weather conditions. ....
7 I missed a lot of school as a child, but I'm am now catching up with my reading and writing. ....
8 Almost twenty percent of people are out of work, which is an incredibly high rate. ....
9 Many people here can't afford food, rent or bills. Most are living on $2 a day. ....
10 There is a shortage of affordable places to live, and these new apartment blocks will help solve the crisis. ....

B Complete the conversation using words from the box.

> endangered   global warming   homelessness
> justice   literacy   overcrowding   poverty
> unemployment

> There's a big problem with ¹.................. in my country. Whenever I go into a city, I see a lot of people who are obviously living on the streets. It isn't a case of there being no housing available, it's just that ².................. because of a shortage of jobs can lead to people ending up on the streets. No job means no home and no home means no job.

> Yeah. And ³.................. in hostels and homeless shelters can mean not even getting a bed for the night. And still so many people live in ⁴.................. even when they do have a home.

> There's no ⁵.................. in this world – some people have so much and others so little.

GRAMMAR

conditionals with conjunctions

2 A Match the sentence beginnings (1–6) with the endings (a–f).

1 Homelessness will continue to be a problem
2 The pace of global warming will start slowing down
3 Provided that there are enough programmes set up to help people,
4 The problem of homelessness in the city can be resolved
5 Languages like Walloon and Ossete could be revived
6 Overcrowding in this area of the city will improve

a on condition that housing and social services are greatly improved.
b as long as we all play our part in reducing our carbon footprint.
c providing that people are encouraged to use them in everyday life.
d so long as the plans to build new housing in the suburbs go ahead.
e unless the government invests in realistic solutions.
f a lack of literacy can become an issue of the past.

B Complete the sentences with the words in the box.

> condition   if not   long as   providing   unless

1 .... governments act right now, the climate will be damaged beyond repaired.
2 We're are always told this isn't the right time. But .... now, then when?
3 Recent findings indicate that as .... we put the work in now, we should be OK.
4 .... that the project gets the funding it needs, it should have a huge impact.
5 The group has said it will stop the protest on .... that their demands are met.

C Choose the correct words to complete the article.

Why there is more and more poverty in wealthy countries

¹**Providing that / Unless** you live in a wealthy country, you can expect a good standard of living, which includes, at the very least, having all your basic human needs met. But wealthy countries have seen an increase in poverty since the global financial crisis that hit in the late 2000s. If this ²**had / hadn't** happened, there ³**won't have been / may not have been** such a huge rise in poverty. Unemployment is partly to blame, and tends to hit those already on very low incomes. ⁴**Unless / As long as** such crises are resolved, the poverty problem becomes broader and deeper, affecting more people, including children, more badly. These problems can start to be resolved ⁵**if / whether** governments implement better policies to help people avoid falling into poverty to begin with.

PRONUNCIATION

3 A 🔊 8.02 | **stress in conditional sentences** | Listen and underline the word that is given the main stress in each sentence.

1 As long as we leave home by seven-thirty, we won't be late.
2 Unless we take action now, the damage will be catastrophic.
3 Provided that endangered languages are taught, they will survive.
4 On condition that the loan is paid back in full, we're happy to approve the request.

B 🔊 8.02 | Listen again and repeat.

LISTENING

4 A 🔊 8.03 | Listen to the introduction to a talk. Which world issue does the speaker focus on?
   a homelessness
   b civil rights
   c low levels of literacy

B 🔊 8.04 | Listen to the rest of the talk. Complete the notes with one or two words in each gap.

- Everyday reading tasks include timetables, labels and ¹_____ to help us find our way around.
- People are more likely to make ²_____ via text message now.
- ³_____ purposes for literacy include staying informed and communicating well.
- Young children can start to acquire knowledge of reading through listening to ⁴_____.
- Visits to a ⁵_____ can be an exciting weekly event.
- Adults may have missed out on gaining literacy skills because of ⁶_____ during childhood.

C 🔊 8.04 | Listen again. Are the statements True (T) or False (F)?

1 The speaker believes literacy is essential for young learners.
2 She argues that older people aren't all as digitally literate as young people.
3 She thinks that text messages have had a negative impact on literacy.
4 She believes that parents should limit children's access to online materials.
5 She argues that there are lots of different ways to make learning to read enjoyable.
6 She's happy that there are now more resources available for adults.

D 🔊 8.05 | Listen to the final line of the lecture and write what you hear. You will hear the sentence only once.

_____

Lesson 8C

HOW TO ... | develop an argument
VOCABULARY | prepositional phrases
PRONUNCIATION | sounding persuasive

VOCABULARY

prepositional phrases

1 A Choose the correct phrase to complete the sentences.

1 **By far / Out of control / On the whole**, older people have fewer online connections than younger ones.
2 **At least / In fact / In order to** create an account, you need to complete the questionnaire.
3 Facebook is still the most used social media platform **by far / at least / in order to**.
4 Social media is great to connect with people but **by far / on the whole / at the same time**, you have to be aware of trolls.
5 I don't have many online friends. **In fact, / By far, / At least**, I only accept requests from people I know.
6 Measures must be put in place to stop online bullying getting **out of control / on the whole / at least**.

B Complete the article about Dunbar's number with the prepositional phrases in the box.

| at least | at the same time | by far | in fact |
| in order to | on the whole | out of control | |

Dunbar's number

According to Professor Robin Dunbar of Oxford University, [1]_____ maintain good relationships, there is a limit to how many friends we can handle. This number is probably a lot lower than the number of online friends you have. [2]_____, it only amounts to about 150 people. Dunbar believes this has been the case since [3]_____ our early hunter-gatherer days.

Through extensive research, Dunbar came to the conclusion that there is a ratio between how big our brains are and how big a social group we can retain. [4]_____, experiments carried out indicate that the 'magic number' is 150. This is because there's only so much information you can hold in your head. [5]_____, other animals have limitations on the size of their social group, too, depending on their brain size.

Now social media has entered the mix, does this number still hold true? Many of us have a more online friends than 'real' friends [6]_____, in some cases reaching thousands. Experts in the field of social media tend to agree with Dunbar's number, even in online communities. Letting your numbers get [7]_____ simply means you'll find it impossible to stay friends with everyone.

How to ...

develop an argument

2 A 🔊 8.06 | Listen to the start of a debate. Number the arguments in the order they are presented.

a Online interactions are less meaningful.
b It's easier to be misunderstood online.
c We can ignore people that we disagree with.

B 🔊 8.07 | Complete the extracts. Listen and check.

1 I'd like to start off _____ that I completely agree that social media has killed the art of conversation.
2 This is true for three _____. Firstly, we no longer have to interact face to face ...
3 _____, we are no longer able to discuss our views in person with someone that we disagree with.
4 It's easier, but it has clearly _____ fewer meaningful interactions.
5 The _____ is often miscommunication and confusion.

PRONUNCIATION

3 🔊 8.08 | **sounding persuasive** | Listen to the extracts. Underline the words that are given extra stress and draw a (/) to show long pauses.

1 I'd like to start off by saying that I completely agree that social media has killed the art of conversation.
2 Firstly, we no longer have to interact face to face with people who disagree with us.
3 Secondly, whereas in the past we had to call or arrange to meet someone we hadn't spoken to in a long while, now we can just fire off a quick message online.

SPEAKING

4 A Complete the extract from a talk with one word in each gap.

I'd like to [1]_____ off by saying that I fully believe in small businesses making use of online platforms to promote their service or products. The [2]_____ suggests that this can be a great way to reach a lot of people quickly. A good [3]_____ of this is beauty products. By uploading regular photos and videos to the right platforms, you can reach huge numbers of people. The obvious [4]_____ of this is that sales will increase dramatically in a short space of time.

The second [5]_____ I'd like to make is that online marketing will save you money. This is [6]_____ for two main reasons. [7]_____, you won't have to pay as much in advertising, and [8]_____, you can do much of the work yourself.

B 🔊 8.09 | Listen and check.

Speak anywhere Go to the interactive speaking practice

56

Lesson 8D

VOCABULARY | phrases with *get*
READING | community-led projects

VOCABULARY

phrases with *get*

1 A Match the sentence beginnings (1–6) with the endings (a–f) to make sentences.

1 Congratulations! Here are the keys. You've finally got
2 Cutting back on spending is the best way to
3 Falling off the horse last month scared me. I need to
4 It's clear to everyone that Sally has got
5 There's no way I would have got
6 It may not feel like it now, but you'll soon get

a a big heart. She has time for everyone.
b to the other side of this.
c somewhere to live!
d find a way to get my confidence back.
e get yourself out of debt.
f to where I am now with the help of my parents.

B Choose the phrase with *get* which describes the following situations.

> get your confidence back   get your life back together
> get out   get somewhere to live   get to the other side
> got a big heart

1 James is lovely – there's nothing he wouldn't do for someone, even people he doesn't like. ....
2 Guess what? I've just paid a deposit on that brilliant flat I told you about. ....
3 You've just got to make it through the next two months, then everything will be fine, I promise. ....
4 It took me a long time to get back on a bike after my accident, but I did it. ....
5 Everything fell apart after being made redundant but I've got a new job and house now. ....
6 Why do you stay in that relationship? I think you should just leave. ....

READING

2 A Read the article. Match the projects (1–5) with the issues that they are designed to help address.

- climate change
- endangered languages
- homelessness
- lack of affordable housing
- literacy

B Read the article again. Complete the sentences with no more than three words or numbers.

1 Orange Sky Laundry washes clothes for homeless people using .... in the back of their vans.
2 Volunteers at the repair café in Buxton fix items such as washing machines and .... for free.
3 Wikitongues has recorded .... different endangered languages.
4 RUSS was set up to .... thirty-six new homes for would-be residents.
5 Literacy Pirates aims to improve the literacy, confidence and .... of local children.

Five community-led projects taking on the big issues

1 Orange Sky Laundry
Australian charity, Orange Sky Laundry, provides a mobile laundry and shower service for people sleeping rough across the country. With the help of donations and hundreds of volunteers, the organisation owns a fleet of vans, each with two washing machines in the back, which it sends out to affected communities.
Set up in 2014 by friends Lucas Patchett and Nicholas Marchesi, Orange Sky Laundry now operates in multiple cities across Australia and New Zealand.

2 Transition Buxton
Transition Buxton works on a range of environmental projects in the town of Buxton in Derbyshire, UK. Their initiatives include a community orchard, a home energy scheme and a repair café. The repair café is a monthly service designed to reduce waste and carbon footprints, by fixing items that would otherwise have been thrown away. Run by volunteers, the group repair everything from washing machines to bicycles – all for free.

3 Wikitongues
This New York-based non-profit organisation offers free resources, training and grants for projects aimed at sustaining and promoting languages. Founded in 2014, one of the charity's key initiatives is their series of Living Dictionaries – free online tools that document thousands of words and phrases from endangered languages. So far, the organisation has recorded videos of over 700 different languages and created hundreds of free resources.

4 Rural Urban Synthesis Society (RUSS)
Tired of the lack of affordable housing in Lewisham in Southeast London, a group of locals formed RUSS in late 2021, to design and self-build thirty-six new houses. The project – which is the largest of its kind in the capital – has given would-be residents the chance to build the homes alongside local volunteers. Residents will also have access to a local community centre, communal garden, shared laundry and a public playground.

5 Literacy Pirates
Literacy Pirates is a charity based in Hackney, London, that provides after-school reading and writing clubs for students whose teachers feel they could do with a bit of extra help. Aimed at children aged 9-12 and led by a group of qualified teachers and trained volunteers, the clubs take place in a series of pirate-themed learning spaces. The charity hopes not only to help improve student literacy, but also to promote confidence and self-esteem.

7-8 REVIEW

GRAMMAR

1 📖 Choose the correct word to complete the sentences.

1 It _____ have been easy moving to a new school and not knowing anyone.
  a can't b might c could
2 You _____ have seen Jurassic Park – everyone has!
  a could b must c couldn't
3 They _____ have got stuck in traffic. It's very busy near the airport.
  a could b can't c couldn't
4 He _____ have called in sick – he didn't look well yesterday.
  a can't b might c couldn't
5 You _____ have practised a lot to be this good.
  a must b can c can't
6 It _____ have been Tom you saw. He's away this weekend.
  a might b must c can't

2 Complete the sentences with the correct form of the verbs in brackets.

1 I wish I _____ (have) more free time at the weekends.
2 If only you _____ (tell) me you'd be out late – I wouldn't have been so worried.
3 You should _____ (practise) your answers before the interview.
4 I wish the dogs _____ (bark) so much at night. I can never get to sleep.
5 If only you _____ (visit) me here in California – it's amazing!
6 You _____ (not take) my car without asking permission.

3 Match (1–5) with (a–e).

1 The book has had brilliant reviews,
2 I love swimming in the sea.
3 Though I'm not very good at surfing,
4 Hard work is important,
5 On the one hand, I enjoy doing it

a although you've got to have fun, too.
b However I only do it the summer.
c but on the other, it takes up a lot of my free time.
d I love being out on the waves.
e though the author didn't think it was her best work.

4 Put the words in the correct order to make sentences with participle clauses.

1 in the capital, / many young people / arriving / to find / struggle / work
2 Miguel / it was / having moved / how noisy / to the city, / was surprised by
3 having finally / Sally / on time / finished / the report, / for once / left work
4 grew up / Teddy / being / brought up with / really fast / much older siblings,
5 Tina / was always / in the gym, / spending / too tired / so many hours / to walk home

5 Rewrite the sentences using the words in brackets.

1 You may park your car here but only stay for an hour.
  You may park here _____ (condition) for an hour.
2 If you don't make the first move, some people won't engage in conversation.
  Some people won't engage _____ (unless) you make the first move.
3 If we finish badminton practice on time, I'll come and meet you.
  I'll come _____ (providing) we finish badminton practice on time.
4 Stay calm and the performance will go well.
  The performance will _____ (long) you stay calm.
5 If enough people come to help, we can clean the park in a couple of hours.
  We can clean the park in a _____ (provided) enough people come to help.

VOCABULARY

6 Complete the news story with the words in the box. There is one item you don't need.

> all-consuming   by chance   fortunate   life-changing
> long-lasting   nineteen-year-old   world-famous

Develop your talent

When [1]_____ Alenka Kos met Anders Bergman [2]_____ on a skiing holiday in Sweden, little did she know that this would be a [3]_____ event. Anders was a medal-winning skier, and he taught Alenka a few techniques to improve her own skiing. In fact, she improved so much during her holiday that Anders, who also ran a ski school, suggested she train as a ski instructor herself.

'I was so [4]_____ to meet Anders when I did,' explains Alenka. 'I'd just finished college and had no idea what I wanted to do next. But skiing's my passion, and once I met Anders, I had this [5]_____ desire to become an instructor and help others ski better. I'm not good enough to compete like Anders does, and I'll never become a [6]_____ athlete, but I've lived in Sweden ever since, and absolutely love my new life here. If there's something you're really interested in, just go for it!'

REVIEW 7–8

7 Complete the sentences with the correct form of the idioms in the box.

> a blessing in disguise   back to the drawing board
> be a piece of cake   miss the boat
> not be someone's cup of tea
> the grass is always greener on the other side

1 Thanks for inviting me to the gig but it's really .... I'd rather stay at home.
2 This weather has been .... If it had been hotter, we'd have suffered during the match.
3 I'll have to go .... and start the table plan again. A few people can't come.
4 That test .... ! I'll probably get 100 percent.
5 I've .... on ticket sales – apparently, they've all just sold out.
6 People think .... , so they're disappointed when they realise it isn't.

8 Complete the sentences with *across*, *down*, *into*, *out*, *over* or *through*.

1 Can you slow .... ? I can't understand you.
2 I'll be going .... a lot of detail about the process, so please make notes.
3 If you break things .... into smaller chunks, they become easier to understand.
4 I'm going to go .... the writing skills again in Thursday's lesson, so please do attend.
5 Can I talk .... a few things with you? I want know how to improve my technique.
6 If you want to get your message .... , you'll have to be more assertive.
7 Oh no! I left something really important .... of my presentation!
8 I don't think I'm ever going to figure .... how to build this wardrobe!

9 Complete the anecdote with the correct form of *go*, *have* or *make*.

Everything ¹................. wrong when we moved house. The removal guys turned up late, and nothing ²................. according to plan after that. I'd carefully wrapped all my valuable items but it didn't ³................. a difference. Two got broken. I ⁴................. a point of writing on the boxes which room the items should be put in, but everything ended up in the wrong place. I thought it ⁵................. sense to move the smaller items out of the house before the furniture, but that left us nowhere to put some of the bigger items. Also, we never ⁶................. the opportunity to thoroughly clean our new house before we moved in.

10 Choose the correct words to complete the sentences.

1 This is a very **exclusive** / **spacious** part of town and houses here cost millions.
2 People spend a lot of money making their homes **secure** / **fashionable** as there are lots of break-ins.
3 The room is so **stylish** / **spacious** that we had to buy some new furniture to fill it.
4 What an **elegant** / **exclusive** room! I love the decoration and layout.
5 Old houses tend to have a lot more **condition** / **character** than new ones.

11 Match the sentence beginnings (1–6) with the endings (a–f).

1 Unemployment can lead to a series of events
2 I attend literacy classes now as an adult because
3 Homelessness isn't a big problem where I live,
4 Overcrowding is a big problem in some countries,
5 The majority of people don't understand what it's like to live in poverty
6 The number of endangered languages is increasing

a with many people competing for the same resources.
b that results in people losing their home and way of life.
c because communication has become more and more globalised.
d I didn't learn to read or write well enough when I was at school.
e and to not even have basic needs such as warmth and shelter.
f but there should be more shelters for people on the street in general.

12 Complete the conversation with the phrases in the box. There is one phrase you don't need.

> at least   at the same time   by far   in fact
> in order to   on the whole   out of control

Steph: Is there a sense of community where you live?
Tom: Yes. It's ¹................. the friendliest place I've ever lived. What about you?
Steph: Well, neighbours don't tend to do much together, but ²................. people are nice enough.
Tom: It's tricky to get the balance right. You want to say 'hi' and chat, but ³................. , you don't want to get in people's faces too much.
Steph: You're right. It's hard if you don't know people, though. Some of the kids' behaviour is ⁴................. . Like, they kick balls against people's houses. I'm not sure how to approach the situation.
Tom: ⁵................. they're playing out instead of being on screens. But you might need to speak to their parents ⁶................. resolve things.

13 Choose the correct word or phrase to complete the sentences.

1 Saira's got a big .... and will help anyone.
  a heart   b back   c life
2 It was hard to get my life back .... after losing my job.
  a the other side   b now   c together
3 Have you got .... to live?
  a where   b the other side   c somewhere
4 It can be hard to get .... of debt.
  a out   b a big   c my life
5 It took years of hard work to get .... I am now.
  a together   b where   c somewhere
6 Simon has got his .... back after failing the audition.
  a side   b heart   c confidence

1–4 CUMULATIVE REVIEW

GRAMMAR

present perfect simple and continuous

1 Use the prompts to write present perfect simple or present perfect continuous sentences.
1. How long / you / learn the violin?
2. You / ever / go / to Russia?
3. I / go to bed / much later / recently
4. I / wait / here / last two and a half hours!
5. Ali / see / the *James Bond* film / three times

infinitive and -ing forms

2 Rewrite the sentences using the correct form of the verbs in brackets.
1. I used to buy groceries on the way home from work.
   I stopped .... (buy) food on the way home.
2. Ask Sheila if she wants to come to the party.
   Remember .... (invite) Sheila to the party.
3. I'll always remember waking up on that beach in Hawaii.
   I'll never forget .... (wake) up on that beach in Hawaii.
4. You need to practise every day to learn anything.
   The way to learn anything is by .... (practise) every day.
5. I'm travelling around Southeast Asia on my gap year.
   My plan is .... (travel) around Southeast Asia on my gap year.

future probability

3 Complete the sentences with the words in the box.

| certain to   due to   going to |
| might   unlikely to   'll |

1. I .... never go travelling on my own because I'm simply not brave enough.
2. I'm .... see Connie today, so could you give her this birthday card, please?
3. We .... go to Japan this year but we haven't made our minds up yet.
4. They are not .... make it to the airport on time if they don't hurry up.
5. She's .... pass her exam on Monday. There's no doubt about it!

relative clauses

4 Complete the sentences with a relative pronoun or '–' if the pronoun can be omitted.
1. Is Bearded Theory the festival .... we first met? I can't remember.
2. The guy .... we spoke to when we first arrived wasn't very helpful.
3. Remember that group .... parents came to the festival with them? How embarrassing!
4. You know that orchestra .... played last night? What was their name again?
5. Look, that's the festival .... I was telling you about the other day.

cleft sentences

5 Complete the text messages with *what* or *it*. Use the correct form of *be* if necessary.

LEX
Hey, Jen – I loved your flash mob in town today.

JEN
Haha! Thanks, Lex. ¹............... our leader, Carlo's idea to organise it. We thought it might be a good way to advertise the dance group. ²............... interesting is that the police didn't try to stop it. They seemed to actually quite enjoy it!

LEX
³............... I liked about it ⁴............... the dance off! I still can't believe you didn't win!

JEN
⁵............... my last move that let me down! Haha! I did fall off a bench after all!

STU
Well, what's next? That's ⁶............... I want to know!

future continuous and future perfect

6 Choose the correct words to complete the sentences.
1. We'll **have finished / be finishing** dinner by the time you get back, but I'll leave some in the fridge for you.
2. At this rate, I'll still **have worked / be working** on this project well into the new year.
3. She might **have finished / be finishing** with it by now. Why don't you go and ask her?
4. Call me later. I'll **have spoken / be speaking** to Jacob by then, so I should know more.
5. I'll **have finalised / be finalising** the contract by mid-afternoon, so I'll send it across after that.

VOCABULARY

personality adjectives

7 Complete the sentences with the adjectives in the box.

| adventurous   ambitious   argumentative |
| curious   stubborn |

1. I must admit, I am quite .... Once I've made up my mind, I rarely change it.
2. Young children are so .... about the world. They want to know everything!
3. I'd say I'm pretty .... I've flown in a helicopter, climbed a mountain – I've even rafted through the Amazon!
4. My mum was a pretty .... businesswoman. She'd become a CEO by her mid-forties.
5. Those two are so .... They're always falling out with each other.

CUMULATIVE REVIEW 1-4

suffixes

8 Complete the job advert with the adjective form of the words in brackets.

> **Food Taster**
>
> We're looking for people to taste test our new range of vegan products. This is a very ¹_____ (practice) job, and you don't need to be ²_____ (experience) in the role as on-the-job training is provided.
>
> Our workplace is fairly ³_____ (relax) and we're looking for people who are ⁴_____ (rely) and ⁵_____ (optimist). In return for your tasting expertise, we offer ⁶_____ (real) rates of pay and excellent benefits.

science and technology

9 Match the definitions with the words in the box. There are three words you don't need.

> analyse findings predict remotely researcher
> smart tech industry virtual reality

1 images and sounds created by a computer that seem real to the user _____
2 controlled by computers, so it appears to act in an intelligent way _____
3 information discovered as a result of a study _____
4 to examine something carefully to understand or explain it _____
5 from a distance _____

health and lifestyle

10 Complete the phrases with the words in the box.

> do expand keep (×2) stay transform

1 _____ your lifestyle
2 _____ mentally active
3 _____ in shape
4 _____ regular workouts
5 _____ your horizons
6 _____ up your progress

lifestyle adjectives

11 Choose the correct words to complete the sentences.

1 I suppose my job is pretty **unique / tedious** in that I can be based anywhere in the world.
2 He lives in quite a **unique / modest** house, considering he's worth millions.
3 I've been told I'm full of crazy ideas, but I think I'm very **modest / ordinary**!
4 This project is so **tedious / ordinary**. I can't wait till it's finished.
5 Conditions at sea can be pretty **modest / harsh** and it's not fun being caught in a storm.

festivals; the environment

12 Complete the information about a festival.

> acts attracts carbon footprint festival-goers
> organisers renewable sustainable venues

> A Greener Festival is a not-for-profit organisation which helps festival ¹_____ around the world to make their events more sustainable and reduce their ²_____. This lessens their environmental impact and ³_____ those keen to make a difference, including not only ⁴_____ but the musicians themselves. The organisation's Woodstock Principles, launched on Earth Day 2008, are a set of ten ideas which encourage anyone in the music industry to hold more environmentally-friendly events. These principles include things like using ⁵_____ energy and reducing waste at ⁶_____, as well as selling greener merchandise. It also encourages fans and ⁷_____ alike to adopt ⁸_____ practices.

How to …

13 Complete the conversation with one word in each gap.

Pippa: I'm absolutely passionate ¹_____ reading. I'm not a big ²_____ of science fiction or fantasy, but I'll read anything else. You?
Max: I'm ³_____ keen on sci-fi either. I've got really ⁴_____ crime recently.
Pippa: Me too! ⁵_____ I love about it is trying to guess who did it.
Max: Well, I've just finished a great Harlan Coben mystery. I'd ⁶_____ happy to lend it you.

14 Complete the text with the words in the box.

> fact impression sure thought way

> Look our new neighbours! I'd have ¹_____ they'd stay in more now they've got children. I get the ²_____ they've got a lot of money. I'm not 100 percent ³_____ but I think they've even got a live-in nanny to look after the kids. There's no ⁴_____ I'd have let someone else bring our kids up! I know for a ⁵_____ I'd have done a better job myself!

15 Complete the conversation with one word in each gap.

Emir: Do you watch much TV?
Burcu: I use streaming services like Netflix, Amazon Prime and _____ on.
Emir: I've just finished a good Scandi noir series.
Burcu: What *is* Scandi noir? Is it sort _____ dark crime or something?
Emir: Crime stories set in Scandinavian countries. Sometimes weird _____ happens. It's good. I like the scenery _____ everything. I read the subtitles. I find it _____ of interesting listening to the languages.
Burcu: Are there many?
Emir: Languages? Maybe – five _____ so.

5–8 CUMULATIVE REVIEW

GRAMMAR

past perfect simple and continuous

1 **Complete the sentences with the correct form of the verbs in brackets.**
   1 By the time I got home, the kids _____ (eat) all the pizza and there was none left for me!
   2 I had to rush back home because I suddenly realised I _____ (leave) the door unlocked.
   3 I was exhausted by lunchtime because I _____ (do) a lot of heavy lifting.
   4 She _____ (ring) for ages before Matt finally answered his phone.
   5 I _____ (always love) dancing so was keen for my son to give classes a try.

past plans and intentions

2 **Rewrite the sentences using the verbs in brackets.**
   1 I planned to see Shelly but I forgot.
      I _____ Shelly but I forgot. (supposed)
   2 Ben intended to go to university, but decided to get a job instead.
      Ben _____ to university, but decided to get a job instead. (going to)
   3 I thought about getting a new hairstyle but I'm not going to now.
      I _____ a new hairstyle but I'm not going to now. (considering)
   4 I thought I'd see you at the market but I didn't.
      I _____ you at the market but I didn't. (expecting)
   5 We had made a plan to go to Goa, but had to cancel.
      We _____ to Goa, but had to cancel. (planning)

necessity, prohibition and permission

3 **Choose the correct words to complete the sentences.**
   1 Sorry I wasn't in when you called. I **must / had to** go to the dentist.
   2 Ball games are not **permitted / forbidden** on the grass. Please use the pitch provided.
   3 I **mustn't / couldn't** go to the concert in the end because I had a bad cold.
   4 Are we **allowed / forbidden** to use our phone here?
   5 Look at the state of your hair! We **can / must** get it cut – it's far too long.

past modals of deduction

4 **Complete the sentences with the correct form of the verbs in brackets and a modal of deduction.**
   1 It _____ (be) easy for Jo to apologise when both parties were to blame.
   2 It _____ (be) exciting for you to see Emily in her first TV show!
   3 I _____ (always have) mild asthma, but who knows?
   4 I think he _____ (decide) to go home – he didn't look very well earlier.
   5 They _____ (travel) by train because they were all cancelled.

wish, if only, should have

5 **Choose the correct options to complete the sentences.**
   1 I wish **we left / we'd left** earlier because now we'll miss the train!
   2 You shouldn't **have told / tell** them you were fired from your last job.
   3 If only **I tried / I'd tried** a bit harder at school when I was younger.
   4 I wish you **had told / will tell** me you were coming!
   5 If only **they'll be / they'd be** a bit quieter next door

participle clauses

6 **Complete the anecdote with the correct form of the verbs in brackets.**

> ¹ _____ (wake) up suddenly in the middle of the night I shouted, 'Who's ringing the doorbell?!'
> ² _____ (climb) out of bed, I went downstairs to open the door. Having ³ _____ (unlock) it, I said, 'We haven't actually *got* a doorbell'.
> ⁴ _____ (sit) back in bed, puzzled, I looked up why I'd been so convinced I'd heard a doorbell ring.
> ⁵ _____ (have) now read lots about this phenomenon, I know it's called a 'hypnagogic hallucination' and it occurs when we're not fully asleep!

VOCABULARY

work and careers; areas of work

7 **Complete the sentences with the correct form of the words in the box.**

   accountancy   advance   publishing
   retrain   start out

   1 My cousin works for a large _____ firm. He's always enjoyed working with numbers.
   2 I've decided to _____ as a beautician. I like styling hair but I want to try something new.
   3 My dad _____ in banking, but switched to the antiques business in his forties.
   4 My boss keeps suggesting I try for promotion but I'm not interested in _____ my career.
   5 I wouldn't mind working in _____. I love reading books of all kinds, and I'd like to be an editor.

prefixes

8 **Complete each word with a prefix.**
   1 Stop being so _____patient! I'll get you something to eat as soon as I've finished this.
   2 I've _____written the conclusion to my essay because I didn't think it included everything.
   3 A _____heading is a line or two that gives more information about something you're going to read.
   4 Mario's being a bit _____honest about where he was on Saturday. He's not telling the truth.
   5 I think I've _____understood the instructions for this table – why does it look so weird?

CUMULATIVE REVIEW 5–8

reporting verbs

9 Choose the correct words to complete the sentences.
1. I **suggested** / **admitted** taking the car to the garage so they can take a look at it.
2. He **apologised** / **denied** transferring the money from our joint account into his own!
3. The officer **insisted** / **accused** it was me on the CCTV footage, but I wasn't even in the area.
4. The woman **refused** / **doubted** to move her car so I could get out of my driveway.
5. I really **deny** / **regret** spending so much of my savings on that terrible car.

compound adjectives

10 Complete the biography with the compound adjective form of the words in brackets.

Kim Peek (1951–2009) was a _____ (world / famous) savant. In fact, if you've ever seen the _____ (wide / respect) 1980s film *Rain Man*, you might be aware that it was based on him. Kim could recall 10,000 books he'd read, which would be incredibly _____ (time / consume) for us, but Kim could memorise a whole book in an hour.

Kim had been born a savant: there was no sudden _____ (life / change) event that altered his brain and left him with _____ (long / last) effects. The _____ (fifty-eight / year / old) died in 2009, but his memory lives on.

chance

11 Complete the sentences with the words in the box.

by chance   fortunate   random
unexpected   unfortunate

1. Winners are chosen at _____. The names are pulled out of a hat.
2. It was _____ that your flight was cancelled.
3. Josef leaving the company was totally _____.
4. I found that book you wanted _____ when I was looking for something else.
5. You're very _____ to be able to play the piano like that. I wish I could play an instrument!

phrasal verbs: explaining

12 Complete the definitions with the words in the box.

figure out   get across   go over
leave out   talk through

1. If you _____ something _____ to other people, you make something understood.
2. If you _____ something _____, you understand it after thinking about it for a while.
3. If you _____ something _____, you don't include something or someone.
4. If you _____ something _____, you discuss something thoroughly.
5. If you _____ something, you repeat it carefully until it is clear.

describing homes and living conditions

13 Choose the correct words to complete the sentences.
1. To make your house completely **stylish** / **secure**, invest in a good alarm.
2. This house is full of **character** / **condition**. Just look at the ceilings.
3. There is a very **exclusive** / **spacious** garden, with room for a pool!
4. This is an **elegant** / **exclusive** area of town where many famous people live.
5. The house was in excellent **condition** / **character** – nothing needed doing.

world issues

14 Complete the sentences with the words in the box.

endangered   homeless   housing   literacy   poverty

1. My first language is _____ because no one uses it anymore.
2. Low levels of _____ can lead to a lack of confidence and progress.
3. There simply is not enough _____ for everyone who needs a place to live.
4. There are way too many _____ people and this is terrible in such a wealthy country.
5. Too many people live in _____ and struggle to pay their bills.

How to …

15 Complete the conversation with one word in each gap.

Lara: I can't ¹_____ anything to work! There's something ²_____ with my laptop and now there's a ³_____ with the fridge!
Jo: It might be ⁴_____ having a look at that little dial thing. Maybe it's too low. ⁵_____ don't you try getting a tech guy to take a look at your laptop?

16 Complete the conversation with the words in the box.

advice   hope   might   should   suggest

Al: Can you give me some ¹_____ on clothes?
Sue: Well, I ²_____ you don't take this the wrong way, but you do put strange colours together!
Al: Do I? What would you ³_____, then?
Sue: It ⁴_____ be a good idea to look through some magazines or online.
Al: I haven't got time! I need something for a wedding next week. What do you think I ⁵_____ do?

17 Complete the instructions with one word in each gap.

To ¹_____ with, get all your ingredients together. The next ²_____ is to chop the onion and put the water on to boil. Once ³_____ done that, fry the onions. When the water is boiling, add the pasta. Now add the tomatoes to the pan. ⁴_____ not essential that you stir the sauce continuously, but ⁵_____ careful it doesn't burn. If you ⁶_____, you could add some basil. The final ⁷_____ involves stirring the pasta into the sauce.

63

1–8 CUMULATIVE REVIEW

GRAMMAR

while, whereas and whilst

1 Match the sentence beginnings (1–8) with the endings (a–h) to make sentences with *while*, *whereas* and *whilst*.

1 While Daisy is quite confident and outgoing,
2 Whereas the north is experiencing heavy snow,
3 Naoko loves extreme activities like rock-climbing,
4 Whilst I enjoy Paulo's company,
5 While my partner loves folk music,
6 Whilst I often forget where I've put things,
7 Whereas most people in my class went on to uni,
8 Whilst my daughter is loud and rebellious,

a whereas I prefer staying in with a good book.
b it's quite warm in the rest of the country.
c I do at least take care of my possessions.
d I decided to go travelling for a year.
e I couldn't listen to his stories for hours on end!
f I much prefer bands like Deftones and Metallica.
g my son is fairly calm and thoughtful.
h her brother Rob is lacking in self-belief.

quantifiers

2 Complete the conversation with the words in the box. There are two extra words.

| all   each   few   good   handful   little |
| majority   minority   number   several |

Dan: Hey, so have you ever been foraging?
Alexis: Er, I don't think so! What is it?
Dan: You know, it's when you go out into nature to look for food. You collect it, bring it home and use it in your cooking. Very ¹............... people do it, but I suppose that's a good thing – more food for everyone else!
Alexis: Are you talking about picking mushrooms and berries and things? I *have* done that once, but I only collected a ²............... of blackberries – it was a bit of waste of time to be honest.
Dan: Well, you've got to go to the right place at the right time. The ³............... of people who do it go regularly and know all of the best spots. There's a ⁴............... deal of food out there if you know what you're doing – and it's ⁵............... free!
Alexis: But doesn't that cause problems for, like, the ecosystem or whatever?
Dan: Not if you do it carefully and thoughtfully. You can't just grab a large ⁶............... of things all from the same place. If ⁷............... person takes just a ⁸............... of what's available, nothing suffers. And you get free food out of it! What's not to like?

do and did for emphasis

3 Rewrite the sentences using the correct form of *do* or *did* to add emphasis.

1 I've gone off them now, but I used to like a band called Zeds.
   I .... a band called Zeds, but I've gone off them now.
2 Who's this song by? I really like it.
   I .... – who's it by?
3 I live-stream a lot of concerts, but I don't go to them.
   I don't go to a lot .... live-stream them.
4 I'm surprised that you still work at Wonderland Theme Park!
   You .... Wonderland Theme Park, do you?
5 I want to go on holiday. But I don't want to go with Candice.
   I .... on holiday, just not with Candice.

passives

4 Complete the sentences with the correct passive forms of the verbs in brackets.

1 It .... generally .... (accept) that teenagers need much more sleep than adults.
2 Students at Downheel High .... (expect) to be punctual and look smart.
3 It .... (recommend) that everyone gets between seven and nine hours' sleep a night.
4 In the past it .... (think) that the sun orbited the Earth and the Earth was flat.
5 In the 1970s, it .... (believe) that chimpanzees could be taught to speak.
6 A large storm .... (report) out at sea, so the 2 p.m. ferry has been cancelled.
7 It .... (decide) that the car park would close at midnight, but no one knew about it.
8 It .... (suggest) that video games help develop problem-solving skills and relieve stress.

non-defining relative clauses for comments

5 Complete the sentences using a relative clause and the prompt in brackets to add a comment.

1 The post came early this morning, *which was a surprise*. (a surprise)
2 I've finally passed my grade 2 violin exam, ...! (a relief)
3 I've got a younger sister, ... (get on well with)
4 I grew up in the suburbs, ... (extremely boring)
5 My alarm clock went off in the middle of the night, ... (annoying)
6 Everyone got a bonus this year except his department, ... (seems unfair)
7 Belle has settled into university life well, ... (great to hear)
8 Tom's got a new French teacher, ... (enjoys being taught by)

CUMULATIVE REVIEW 1–8

reported orders, requests and advice

6 Read the weather report. Then, complete the reported sentences using the correct form of the verbs in brackets.

> 'The weather looks set to be wild and windy this weekend with Storm Norman on the way. It would be wise to avoid any unnecessary travel and ensure your property is secured. The winds are likely to be particularly strong in the north of the country. Be very careful when out and about as there could be flying debris. Rain might cause flooding in some areas. Please follow the weather warnings for your local area.
> That's all for now – have a safe and pleasant evening.'

1 The reporter .... (say) that the weather .... (look) set to be wild and windy that weekend.
2 He .... (advise) people to avoid unnecessary travel and ensure their property .... (be) secured.
3 He .... (warn) that the winds .... (be) likely to be particularly strong in the north of the country.
4 He .... (recommend / be) very careful when out and about as there could be flying debris.
5 He .... (suggest / follow) your local weather warnings.
6 He .... (wish) everyone a safe and pleasant evening.

adverbials of concession

7 Choose the correct words to complete the sentences.
1 The car broke down on the motorway which was scary. **On the one hand / However**, we did get a free lift home!
2 **On the one hand / Although** I'd seen the neighbour around, I'd never spoken to him before.
3 **Though / However** I enjoy most kinds of food, I'd have to say Japanese is my favourite.
4 I'm not into grime music, **on the other hand / although** I do like this particular song.
5 **However / Although** I usually love sunny weather, it's way too hot for me here!
6 **Though / However** my friends all live nearby, I don't see them very often because we're all so busy.
7 **On the one hand / Though** I do really enjoy skiing, I don't really like other winter sports.
8 I've travelled all over the world. **However, / Although** I've never visited Europe.

conditionals with conjunctions

8 Rewrite the sentences using the words in brackets.
1 Children can go on the rides, but only if they are over one metre tall.
   Children can go on the rides .... (condition)
2 You need to come and get your lunch now or it will go cold.
   .... come and get it now. (unless)
3 I'll go with you to the concert but only if we don't stand at the front.
   .... at the front. (provided)
4 We'll make it in time for the film if we leave right now.
   We'll make it in time for the film .... (long)
5 You can go out with your friends but you must be home by ten o'clock.
   .... , you can go out with your friends. (so)

How to …

9 Complete the conversation with one word in each gap.

Larry: Climbing is so dangerous, I don't think it's fair on climbers' families.
Chris: I see your ¹................ , but I wouldn't stop someone doing something they loved.
Larry: That's a ²................ point, I suppose. But on the other ³................ , don't you think it's a bit irresponsible?
Chris: I know what you ⁴................ , but it's up to the people themselves to decide what's right.
Larry: I ⁵................ your point, but I still think it's a very dangerous activity.

10 Number the opening lines of an argument in the correct order.
a Secondly, it's much more difficult to do complex speaking activities online.
b As a result, teachers tend to focus on simple activities that can be completed alone, which isn't enough.
c This is true for three main reasons. Firstly, doing everything online means that children get little to no time to interact outside of the classroom.
d The impact of this is that they will find it much more difficult to develop key social skills.
e I'd like to start off by saying that I completely disagree with the idea that online education is better than being in a physical classroom.

1–8 CUMULATIVE REVIEW

VOCABULARY

collocations about memory; idioms: memory

1 Complete the article with one word in each gap.

Why we immediately forget people's names

We all meet new people regularly, and think we listen carefully to their names when we're introduced. But then, only moments later, it appears that the name went in one [1]_____ and out the other, even for those who fully believe they have perfect [2]_____. Are our short-term [3]_____ so poor?

Not exactly. Research indicates that we are less likely to remember every [4]_____ of conversations that were neither very interesting nor very important to us. The more important it is to remember a name, such as your new manager's, the more likely it is that you'll make the effort to learn it by [5]_____. But sometimes, you want to remember but still can't. The name, given only minutes before slips your [6]_____ completely. Is your memory playing [7]_____ on you? No. You simply underestimated how much effort is required to remember something.

emotions and feelings

2 Choose the correct words to complete the sentences.
1 I'm really passionate **about** / **on** travel.
2 I'm not fond **about** / **of** sweet things.
3 A lot of people are terrified **on** / **of** spiders.
4 I don't think John's keen **on** / **by** Michael.
5 I'm so fed up **by** / **of** my journey to work.

word families

3 Complete the table with the correct form of the words.

verb	noun / person	adjective	adverb
[1]_____	research / researcher		
predict	[2]_____	predictable	predictably
		[3]_____	virtually
		remote	[4]_____
analyse	analysis / analyst	analytical	[5]_____
	science / [6]_____	scientific	scientifically

nature

4 Complete the sentences with the words in the box.

| coastline   deserted beach |
| river bank   track   woodland |

1 The company sources wildflowers from along the western _____.
2 The trees in this _____ are unique to this area.
3 This _____ leads all the way to the river.
4 By this time next week, I'll be lying on a _____!
5 The _____ is home to several types of beaver.

lifestyle adjectives

5 Match the sentence beginnings (1–6) with the endings (a–f).
1 Driving on the motorway is so
2 Few people go to Antarctica in winter
3 She's very modest about her achievements
4 Working with children is so rewarding –
5 I lead a pretty ordinary life –
6 Visiting Norway in twenty-four-hour daylight

a because the conditions are so harsh.
b I don't do anything other people don't.
c they're very happy and learn so quickly.
d and never shows off about them.
e was a truly unique experience for me.
f tedious and you can get very tired.

phrasal verbs: performing; phrasal verbs: communication

6 Choose the correct words to complete the review.

Just back from seeing a new performance of *Alice in Wonderland* at my local theatre. The actors [1]**came** / **went** across as confident and well-rehearsed. They even managed to [2]**carry** / **continue** on when someone in the audience dropped something loudly! One of the younger actors [3]**moved** / **messed** up their lines at one point but it didn't matter.

The only negative was that the costumes and stage scenery didn't [4]**live** / **bring** up to expectations. Whoever [5]**put** / **came** up with some of the ideas had some very strange ones! It [6]**put** / **gave** me off at first because it was so strange, but I got used to it after a while!

film and TV

7 Complete the conversation with the words in the box. There are three extra words.

| based   cast   costumes   ending   scene |
| set   soundtrack   subtitles   twist |

Isla: I like films set in other countries. The scenery's great and the [1]_____ is often music from that country.
Neil: Do you? I hate having to read [2]_____.
Isla: I don't mind, as long as the [3]_____ is good. You know, the actors need to be believable.
Neil: Yeah, and I don't mind if they aren't well-known. I like films with a clever [4]_____ at the end, too.
Isla: That you didn't see coming – yes! I like films [5]_____ on books I've read, as well.
Neil: Even though you know the [6]_____?
Isla: Why not? I usually forget storylines anyway!

CUMULATIVE REVIEW 1–8

illness and treatment

8 Choose the correct option (a–c) to complete the sentences.

1 I can't stop sneezing! I'm tired of having _____.
   a antibiotics   b allergies   c asthma
2 I must have _____. I'm going to be sick again!
   a antibiotics   b vaccines   c food poisoning
3 _____ can protect against illnesses.
   a Vaccines   b Allergies   c First aid
4 I've just finished a _____ course, where I learned about basic treatment in an emergency.
   a medication   b vaccine   c first aid
5 People who suffer from _____ sometimes have breathing problems.
   a antibiotics   b asthma   c food poisoning

sleep; exercise; sport: motivation and benefits

9 Choose the correct words to complete the sentences.

1 The main **benefits** / **strengths** of exercise are that you sleep better, look better, and feel better.
2 I prefer gentle exercise that relaxes me, so I fall into a lovely deep **sleep** / **nap** at night.
3 I don't like **high-impact** / **low-impact** activities. I'm always **aerobic** / **exhausted** afterwards.
4 I like to give myself a **discipline** / **challenge** when I exercise, so I try to keep improving my times.
5 They say that **moderate** / **flexibility** exercise at least three times a week helps you sleep better.

time expressions

10 Complete the sentences with the words in the box. You need to use one of the words twice.

| moment   opportunity   threat   time |

1 Oh, hello! Come in! You're just in _____ for something to eat.
2 The future of the Arctic is under _____ from global warming and we must act faster.
3 They managed to get the cows off the track and not a _____ too soon – a train was coming.
4 Unfortunately, _____ has already run out for some species and they're now extinct.
5 Your window of _____ to get the tickets is short, so you'd better hurry.

video conference calls

11 Choose the correct words to complete the text.

My ¹ **internet connection** / **volume** has never been great, but today my screen was ² **muted** / **frozen** from the start of the call, and it was almost impossible to carry on. The ³ **link** / **host** of the meeting was getting really annoyed and had to ⁴ **invite** / **get in** me back several times. When everything *was* working, there was either an ⁵ **echo** / **internet connection** or there was a ⁶ **link** / **delay**, so I kept speaking over people.

collocations with *get* and *take*

12 Complete the sentences with the correct form of *get* or *take*.

1 I'm sorry, but you've _____ that completely wrong. I've never even been here before.
2 Please don't _____ this personally, but I don't think that colour suits you.
3 I wish I'd stayed at home. I _____ soaked on the way to the station.
4 Let's watch something nice on TV and _____ your mind off things for a while.
5 Are you glad you've _____ all that off your chest?

idioms: regrets

13 Match the idioms (1–5) with the definitions (a–e).

1 be a piece of cake
2 a blessing in disguise
3 miss the boat
4 the grass is always greener on the other side
5 not be (someone's) cup of tea

a lose an opportunity
b not be a favourite or well-suited thing or activity
c something that seems bad but later seems good
d be very easy to do
e a situation seems attractive but may not really be

collocations with *go*, *have* and *make*

14 Complete the sentences with the correct form of *go*, *have* and *make*.

1 My parents always _____ a point of reading me and my brother a bedtime story at night.
2 I don't _____ much in common with my sister but we get on well enough.
3 These wardrobe instructions don't _____ sense. Where does this piece go?
4 Unfortunately, the trip didn't _____ according to plan. We kept missing transport connections.
5 Everything _____ wrong yesterday: my car broke down, I was burgled and I lost my purse!

prepositional phrases

15 Complete the sentences with the phrases in the box. There are two extra phrases.

| at least   at the same time   by far   in fact |
| in order to   on the whole   out of control |

1 _____ make sure the parcel arrives tomorrow, you'll have to send it with our special service.
2 I like Tim _____, but I don't really get his sense of humour.
3 _____ the best way to keep rice fresh is to freeze it as soon as it's cooked.
4 _____ three students in my class have the same bicycle and it gets a bit confusing.
5 Those children are completely _____. They need to be taught how to behave properly.

AUDIOSCRIPTS

UNIT 1

Audio 1.01
1 She's never been to Poland.
2 How long have you been studying in Manchester?
3 What's he been up to this week?
4 I've been trying to book flights to Mexico all morning.
5 She's been waiting here for the last four hours.

Audio 1.02
Presenter: Now, here to tell us all about her latest book, *Who Am I? An exploration of identity,* is author and psychologist, Meg Harper. Meg, welcome to the show.
Meg: Thanks for having me.
Presenter: So, Meg – first things first, what does 'identity' really mean?
Meg: Well, that's actually a pretty big question. But essentially, identity is based on four main areas – your personality traits, so whether you're curious or argumentative, stubborn or outgoing; your likes and dislikes, from your taste in music to your favourite food; your moral code, so what you consider to be right and wrong; and the things that motivate you – you know, what gets you out of bed in the morning. Anyone with a strong sense of self would be able to describe these aspects of their identity fairly easily.
Presenter: And is that important? Do we need to have a clear sense of self?
Meg: Yeah, I think it's really important. Your sense of self affects all aspects of your life, from the job you choose to the relationships you form. If you're not sure who you are, it can be difficult to know what you want and you might struggle to make important decisions. Knowing exactly who you are also means you know what you like about yourself and what you need to work on, which can only be a good thing.
Presenter: OK, so where does our identity come from?
Meg: Well, a lot of it seems to come from our parents. They give us a clear sense of what's right and wrong. Both explicitly … so they tell us … And, perhaps more importantly, through their actions.
Presenter: So, they need to obey the rules themselves?
Meg: Exactly. They're effectively a model for how to act. You know, if we see them working hard, we're more likely to have a strong work ethic ourselves when we grow up. If they often get angry or act aggressively towards people, we may think that's an acceptable way to behave, too.
Presenter: Right. And is that it then – whatever we picked up in childhood we're stuck with?
Meg: No, not at all. It isn't something that's fixed. Your identity continues to develop throughout your life. Certainly, as teenagers we often begin to question what we've been taught, to rebel against the values and behaviours modelled by our parents. And as we grow up, we form new relationships and have new experiences – all of which feeds into our sense of who we are.
Presenter: OK, so finally – what would you say to anyone who is feeling a bit lost and doesn't know who they are?
Meg: Don't worry, you'll get there in the end! Explore and experiment, find out what you like doing and who you identify with.

Audio 1.03
Explore and experiment, find out what you like doing and who you identify with.

Audio 1.04
1 My short-term memory is better than my long-term memory.
2 I've got perfect recall when it comes to phone numbers!
3 This song brings back a lot of childhood memories.

Audio 1.05
Olivia: Shall we go backpacking this summer? It'd be great for the three of us to go on an adventure together!
Amy: Backpacking's not really my kind of thing. I'd much rather stay in a hotel.
Chloe: I'd be happy to go backpacking, but if Amy's not sure, let's just do something else.
Amy: Sorry, it's just that I'm not a big fan of camping. Or sharing rooms in hostels for that matter!
Olivia: Well, we don't have to stay in budget accommodation. How about if we go to lots of different places, but stay in some decent hotels?
Amy: OK. Cool. So, where do you want to go?
Chloe: Well, I'd love to go to Thailand. The beaches there look amazing!
Olivia: Hmmm … I'd be happy to do a bit of sunbathing, but I don't want to do it all day! I want to actually go and *do* stuff as well. I'd much rather go to Japan, then we can visit all the old buildings and eat lots of sushi!
Amy: Isn't Japan really expensive though? How about travelling around Europe instead? Does that sound like a plan?
Olivia: Perfect!
Chloe: Sure!

Audio 1.06
1 I'm quite fond of boat trips, actually. They're a great way to see the city.
2 The kids aren't keen on trying unusual foods.
3 Dan's terrified of driving in foreign countries and so am I!
4 I'm not really into visiting museums. I find a lot of them really boring.
5 I always feel nervous about getting lost when I'm in a new city.
6 Katie's quite passionate about culture and the arts.

Audio 1.07
Hi, I'm Jack. I'm passionate about learning languages and I've been studying them for a few years now. The thing I love about languages is that they give you lots of insight into new cultures. I can't stand hearing people shouting loudly at waiters in English when they're in another country. I'd rather give it a go and get it wrong than not try at all. I'm quite ambitious when it comes to learning languages and I can speak three pretty fluently now!

Audio 1.08
Good morning, everyone. Today I'll be talking about the five main personality traits, which are openness, conscientiousness, extroversion, agreeableness and neuroticism.
Now, whilst you may not recognise some of these big words, these five traits are, according to psychologists, the most commonly studied characteristics of personality, and we all score more highly on some traits and lower on others. There is no perfect combination, so you won't need to worry about that when we do a little personality test later on!
Let's start with openness. This personality trait is to do with your interest in the world. If you're keen to get

AUDIOSCRIPTS

involved with activities you've never tried before, or enjoy discussing concepts you've never heard of, you're an open person. Whereas open people tend to be comfortable with unfamiliar situations, and feel naturally curious, people who are less open may prefer routines and familiar ideas instead. Let's move on to conscientiousness. If you're usually punctual, do what you say you'll do, and take responsibility for your actions, then you're a conscientious person. To put that in an educational context, you're the student who hands in work on time, does the recommended reading and attends all your lectures, whereas in your social life, you'll never leave anyone waiting and people will know they can depend on you.

You'll probably be familiar with the term 'extrovert' and 'introvert'. If you're an extrovert, you might be very enthusiastic and love spending time with people. It's likely that no one would ever call you shy and you're the first one up on the dance floor at parties, while other people are only just warming up!

Would you describe yourself as a kind person who trusts other people and would do anything to lend a hand? If so, you may well have a high level of agreeableness. You will be empathetic, which means you'll get other people's feelings, and you will demonstrate characteristics that show you to be pro-social, in other words, you show concern for others.

Finally, let's turn to neuroticism. People often use this term incorrectly, to suggest that a neurotic person is unpredictable and too emotional. This isn't exactly accurate, though someone who demonstrates high neuroticism will probably experience more negative emotions, such as depression or self-doubt. That doesn't mean you aren't still a great person!

To sum up, everyone has all five traits to a greater or lesser degree! Thank you.

Audio 1.09

To sum up, everyone has all five traits to a greater or lesser degree!

UNIT 2

Audio 2.01

1 VR is certain to come down in price eventually.
2 Robert's due to start his new job on Monday.
3 Are you going to bring your headset with you?
4 You're unlikely to catch anything out in the open.
5 Joseph is going to study law at university.
6 VR is likely to be in every household by 2030.

Audio 2.02

1 There's a lack of attractive green spaces in my town.
2 Only a handful of people I know live in the countryside.
3 I spend a good deal of time outdoors.
4 Several of the beaches nearby are quite good.
5 Young people who like gardening are in a minority.

Audio 2.03

Hello and welcome to this month's edition of *Soundbites*. I'm your host, Adam Byrne.

Now, when I was growing up, gardening was something that your parents did at the weekend. The thought of helping pull up weeds or mow the lawn never crossed my mind. In fact, it probably would've felt like a punishment! But these days, more and more young people are taking up gardening. A recent survey suggests that over eighty percent of 18–34-year-olds think gardening is 'cool', with many spending up to two hours a week looking after their plants. So, what do they get out of it? I spoke to three young gardeners to find out.

Audio 2.04

1: So, I used to have very little interest in gardening, even though my mum was always out there digging and chopping things down and that.
Anyway, at the time, I was feeling pretty stressed – I'd just started uni and was feeling a bit overwhelmed. Then I read that gardening was a great way of being mindful. You know, focusing on your surroundings as a way of feeling calm and relaxed. So, I started helping mum out in the garden whenever I was home from uni and it worked. I'm not sure whether it's because of the garden itself, or just because I can leave my desk for a while. But it really helps me get away from it all.

2: I live in a high-rise apartment block, so I love getting out into green open spaces whenever I can. But I had absolutely zero interest in gardening till someone here started a rooftop community garden. Over time, I saw how things started growing and became fascinated. I asked if I could get involved and since then I go up there every weekend. I've learned tons about planting and looking after stuff, how much sunlight or water things need, what to do in different seasons, all that kind of thing. We're planning a vegetable plot at the moment, where residents will get free food when it's ready – I can't wait!

3: I'm an outdoors kind of girl and, growing up on the coast, I always loved exploring the beaches, surfing, that kind of thing.
Anyway, I was out walking one day along this amazing stretch of coastline and I came across this … kind of, bright, pink flower growing straight out of the cliff face. I remember being amazed that something so beautiful could grow in such a wild, remote place. Anyway, I took a photo and looked it up when I got home. Then I started reading about all of the other plants that are native to this area and was just kind of hooked from there. I'm so glad I started studying flowers. Now I grow all sorts of things on my balcony overlooking the sea.

Audio 2.05

Now I grow all sorts of things on my balcony overlooking the sea.

Audio 2.06

1 Man: What do you think life on a tiny island would be like?
   Woman: I suppose it depends on how remote it is. Like, if you can hop on a boat and get to the mainland in a few minutes, I'd have thought it wouldn't feel so small.
   Man: I reckon you could easily get cut off though. You know, if the sea's rough and ferries are cancelled.
   Woman: Maybe.

2 Man: Do you think we'll get used to life on the mainland quickly? I mean, we've lived on the island all our lives.
   Woman: I bet we'll settle in in no time! I know for a fact that we're going to meet loads of great people at uni. We'll forget all about this little place!
   Man: There's no way I'll forget home so easily! I love it here!

3 Woman: I can't imagine what life will be like round here in the future.
   Man: I doubt there'll be anyone here in a hundred years' time! Most people will have moved to the cities for work.
   Woman: Hmmm … I'd imagine the farmers will stay.
   Man: I get the impression that once the current farming generation retires, there'll be no one to take over.

69

AUDIOSCRIPTS

Audio 2.07
1 There's no way I'd ever consider travelling solo round the world.
2 I know for a fact that I'd feel like I was in prison on a tiny boat.
3 He's obviously not happy where he is at the moment.
4 You're clearly not someone who wants a conventional lifestyle.
5 Tom's bound to live a life of adventure – he can't keep still!

Audio 2.08 and 2.09
Oli: I'd imagine Kwame's feeling nervous about the play tomorrow.
Cara: It's the first night, right? I get the impression that he's feeling pretty confident, actually.
Oli: Oh, yeah?
Cara: Yes – I know for a fact that he's learned his lines off by heart.
Oli: Well, I'd guess you have to, really. There's no way I could be an actor.
Cara: Why not? I'm one hundred per cent sure that you'd be brilliant at it!
Oli: No, I'd be bound to get stage fright!

UNIT 3

Audio 3.01
1 Glastonbury Festival, which has been running since 1970, attracts over 200,000 visitors.
2 The band, who had never played to such a large crowd before, felt very nervous.
3 The headline act, which will perform this evening, is expected to draw a huge crowd.
4 Billie Eilish, who has sold over 5 million records worldwide, will be on stage at nine.
5 The orchestra, which is bigger than ever, will play on the Sticks stage this afternoon.
6 Woodstock, which took place over three days in 1969, was a turning point in music.

Audio 3.02
1 What I like watching are the less well-known acts.
2 It was Max who left the car unlocked, not me.
3 What sounds better to me is finishing on a minor chord.
4 It's you who likes Italian opera – that's why I got the tickets!

Audio 3.03
Alex: Well, that's the first and last time I'm acting on stage! I mean, it was like, a total disaster!
Katy: Oh, no. What happened? Did you mess up your lines?
Alex: No, I'd practised, like, a thousand times! But my partner did and it all got really confusing. She kept coming out with the wrong lines and sometimes forgot what she was supposed to be saying altogether!
Katy: Oops! That happened to me once. I mean, I was the person forgetting the lines. So embarrassing. The play ran for a week and every time I had to go on stage, I could hardly stand up, I was shaking so much. I was just so scared I'd mess up – and I did, every time! I could tell the other guys were frustrated with me, but they were nice enough not to give me a hard time about it. I mean, it wasn't exactly a professional performance. It was just awful, though. Every day I had to go on stage, it was like the worst day of my life!
Alex: Poor you. I guess I should be kinder about my partner – I suppose she had stage fright.
Katy: Yeah – I mean, you feel as if you're going to die of fright. And I knew my lines, they just wouldn't come out of my mouth. It's like I had a total block.
Alex: Hmm … well that does sound awful. But anyway, on top of that, my costume fell to pieces! I mean, it literally fell off on stage!
Katy: Noooo! I helped to make those costumes! How embarrassing!
Alex: Well, it wasn't too bad. It was only the outer layer. And I think someone else made mine, actually. But then, some of the scenery fell over. There was this tree thing in one corner of the stage and bang! It fell over, just like that.
Katy: No way!
Alex: Yes, way! We had to just leave it there until the interval and the props guys sorted it out then. Oh, and listen to this!
Katy: Go on.
Alex: The lighting failed at one point. Like, there was no light whatsoever on stage. We were in the middle of a scene and the lights just went out.
Katy: I bet your time on stage seemed to go on forever! How did the audience react?
Alex: Actually, some of them got up and left which wasn't very nice to see – but totally understandable. I'd have wanted my money back. But the rest were so kind and just pretended the disasters weren't happening.
Katy: That's the good thing about audiences – they do want you to do well.
Alex: Yeah, they were very kind!

Audio 3.04
1 It was like, a total disaster!
2 I'd practised, like, a thousand times!
3 I could hardly stand up, I was shaking so much.
4 It was like the worst day of my life!
5 You feel as if you're going to die of fright.
6 I bet your time on stage seemed to go on forever!

Audio 3.05
It was still a relief to get off stage at the end of the night!

Audio 3.06
Woman: Have you seen *Squid Game*?
Man: No! Isn't it sort of a horror show?
Woman: Something like that. I'd call it a dramatic thriller, actually. Though there are some bits that aren't that nice to watch.
Man: Hmm, I'm not into that kind of thing.
Woman: Well, I definitely wouldn't recommend it for kids.
Man: Isn't it about adults who have to play games to win loads of money?
Woman: Yeah – they compete in Korean children's games and run around and stuff. But the games are deadly!
Man: I think I'll leave that one to you!

Audio 3.07
1 Woman: Who's that guy who played the thief in *Lupin*?
   Man: It's what's his name – oh, you know!
2 Man: When was the *Great Gatsby* supposed to be set? I loved the costumes.
   Woman: Around the 1920s, I think.
3 Man: How old do you think the actor in *Maid* is?
   Woman: I'd say she's young-ish … maybe late 20s?
4 Woman: Did you enjoy watching *the Originals*?
   Man: It was OK. It's sort of for a younger audience, really.
5 Man: Is *Money Heist* a dark story?
   Woman: I suppose it is, a bit. But I like that kind of thing.

AUDIOSCRIPTS

Audio 3.08
1 I love getting caught up in a good mystery series.
2 I like the film. It's sort of a combination of action and thriller.
3 I love dramas that are based on real events.
4 *The Crystal Maze*? Oh, that's where they run around and find crystals or something like that, isn't it?

Audio 3.09 and 3.10
Peter: Have you seen that TV programme, *The Crown*?
Alex: Yeah. I've watched the first series.
Peter: What's it about?
Alex: It's about the British Royal Family. Each series concentrates on a different period of time and the events that took place then. It's a bit slow in places for me, but it's interesting enough.
Peter: Does it show real events and stuff? Or is it all made up?
Alex: It's based on real things that happened, but I think they sort of use a bit of artistic licence – you know, they don't really know what people said or anything so they have to make that up.

Audio 3.11
Hello and welcome to ClickBeat – the show in which my panel and I discuss all things music. Now, today we're focusing on a genre that really does divide opinion – jazz. What is it about this style of music that some people love and others seem to hate? Well, here to help us answer that question is jazz musician Elijah Kegan and music critic Bethany Cartwright. Elijah, Bethany – welcome to the show.

Audio 3.12
Presenter: So, Bethany – what is it about jazz that divides opinion so much?
Bethany: I think partly because it's unpredictable, and it can be difficult to make sense of if you aren't a trained musician. That's because jazz musicians often improvise. In other words, they make music up as they go along, so as a listener, you don't know where it's going next. That can be confusing, as time signatures keep changing. What I mean by that is that you might start out counting one, two, three, four and then find the rhythm's changed to one, two, three, four, five. Counting five beats or seven beats or whatever is very different to most of the music we listen to. It can be tricky to keep track of what's happening. It can create feelings of discomfort, and when we're made to feel uncomfortable by something, we're more likely not to enjoy it.
Presenter: Interesting. Elijah, what do you think?
Elijah: Obviously, I'm a big fan of jazz! I couldn't live without it. Some jazz is very accessible. You'll recognise lots of jazz tunes and tap your feet to them. There's this technique in jazz known as 'noodling'. That's when the music diverts away from the main tune and it can sound quite messy and noisy – though there *is* structure and tune there if you listen for it. I think mainly it's down to the sound – when you have, say, a saxophone involved, it can be quite high pitched and sound like it's screaming. I think that's why some people can't stand it.
Presenter: What do you both think could help people to enjoy jazz more? Or, do they really need to?
Elijah: I do think they're missing out, personally. It's got an interesting history. It's very creative and there are some great tunes and beats – like those ones that get your feet tapping. You don't have to listen to the 'hard core' stuff that serious jazz fans listen to.
Bethany: Elijah's right. There's lots of more sort of basic, structured jazz out there which is a good introduction to the genre. No one *has* to listen to anything they don't want to – but when you give things a go, you often develop new passions for things and it opens your mind.
Presenter: All right, well I think it's time we listened to some, don't you? Coming up next is Duke Ellington's …

Audio 3.13
All right, well I think it's time we listened to some, don't you?

UNIT 4
Audio 4.01
1 By this time next week, I'll have finished this project.
2 Hopefully, I'll have cut out meat entirely by then.
3 With any luck, we'll have bought a house by then.
4 Come round at 7 p.m. – we'll have eaten dinner by then.
5 By this time next week, you'll have graduated from university!

Audio 4.02
1 It was thought that eating cheese before bedtime gives you nightmares.
2 It's been suggested that using your phone in bed makes it harder to drop off.
3 It's believed that up to fifteen percent of the population are sleepwalkers.
4 It's estimated that most people sleep for fewer than seven hours a night.

Audio 4.03
Presenter: Welcome back to the show. Today, we're taking tips from good sleepers across the country with the aim of tackling insomnia! Next on the line is Rob from Lancashire. Rob – what do you do to help you drop off?

Audio 4.04
Presenter: Rob – what do you do to help you drop off?
Rob: Well, I used to use this sleep tracker – in fact, I got a bit obsessed with it. I was told exactly how much deep sleep I was getting, when I was awake and what my total hours' sleep was. I'd check it every morning and I reckon I got less sleep because I was so concerned about whether or not I was getting enough of the 'right' kind! You can't change things, so it's all a bit pointless. My advice is to forget the tracker and focus on techniques for chilling out – it worked for me!
Presenter: Thanks, Rob! Next on the line is Jenna, from Birmingham. Jenna what works for you?
Jenna: I've been an insomniac since I finished university. I think it started with getting all anxious. I kept thinking, 'What will I be doing this time next year? Will I have found a job?', that kind of thing. I'd be so exhausted that I'd need naps during the day – and then the whole vicious circle started again once I got into bed. So, I did a bit of research and discovered an article that said you should stop thinking of yourself as a bad sleeper. I guess it's some kind of reverse psychology. Anyway, I started saying more positive things to myself. It took practice to get anywhere near believing it, but eventually it sank in and now I sleep much better.
Presenter: Great advice, Jenna. I'm sure some of our listeners can relate to that. OK, now let's talk to Álvaro. Álvaro, good morning! What do you do to tackle insomnia?

AUDIOSCRIPTS

Álvaro: OK, well, this one might sound a bit weird but I read about it online.
Presenter: Go on!
Álvaro: Nuts! I mean, eating nuts – they make you sleepy! I don't mean right before you go to bed but just eating them on a regular basis. They've got loads of nutrients in them that are associated with sleep, apparently, and it's been recognised that they do something to brainwave frequencies – whatever that means. Anyway, it helps me. The ones that work best are peanuts.
Presenter: Very interesting! Thank you. We've just got time for one last call … Sonya from Edinburgh. Sonya – what's your tip?
Sonya: I stare into the darkness when I'm in bed rather than shutting my eyes and willing myself to go to sleep. Levels of the sleep hormone are increased that way, apparently. It kind of works, weirdly! I also heard that you should try to stay awake as long as you can if you're having problems dropping off. It has some sort of opposite effect – I've not tried that yet, though!
Presenter: OK, thanks Sonya. Well, that's about it for today's show.

Audio 4.05

Thanks to all of our callers for their advice!

Audio 4.06

Amy: So, have you ever done micro-HIIT training?
Ollie: Is that the one where you push yourself really hard for like, three minutes?
Amy: Yeah, that's right! It sounds ridiculously difficult! Sounds like too much effort to me!
Ollie: I know what you mean, but it's supposed to be really good for you and the best thing is it doesn't take very long!
Amy: Well, that's true.
Ollie: The other thing I was reading about was Everesting. Have you ever heard of that?
Amy: No, what's that? Climbing Everest?!
Ollie: Actually, it's cycling. You cycle up a hill – and back down again – until you've cycled a distance the height of Mount Everest – nearly nine kilometres. It's not that far but you do it in one go. I don't think that'd be too hard.
Amy: I completely disagree. You'd get tired quickly going uphill, I think. You're not an experienced cyclist!
Ollie: I see your point, but I'd soon get fitter.
Amy: That's a fair point.
Ollie: On the other hand, I could probably do with finding something more relaxing and low-impact.
Amy: I couldn't agree more! You're under so much pressure at work. How about yogalates? It's a combination of yoga and pilates. You'd increase your strength and de-stress at the same time.
Ollie: That's a good point. And I could do it from home, online. Anyway, what about you? You're more into walking, right?
Amy: I was but I've got really into this virtual training app and I've started running. I love it!

Audio 4.07

1 I agree up to a point, but don't you think the government should play a role, too?
2 I take your point, but that's what footballers expect to get paid.
3 That's a fair point, but don't you think they get enough exercise at school?

Audio 4.08 and 4.09

Marla: Let's do something. It would be a shame to stay in on a day like this.
Dan: I couldn't agree more. What shall we do? Want to try bouldering with me? Come on …
Marla: Climbing over massive rocks all day? No, thanks. It sounds exhausting.
Dan: I know what you mean, but you did say you want to improve your strength a bit …
Marla: That's a fair point, but I've got work tomorrow and I don't want to be worn out.
Dan: You go to the gym all the time – you'll be fine!
Marla: I completely disagree! Last time we went jogging it took me a week to recover!
Dan: All right, I take your point. You do need a lot of stamina. But on the other hand, if you stay here all day, you'll never get fitter!

UNIT 5

Audio 5.01

1 They'd been waiting outside for hours.
2 I'd been looking for a new job.
3 She hadn't been swimming for a while.
4 Had he been climbing before that?
5 He'd been standing at the bus stop for ages.
6 The team had been asking for a pay rise for months.

Audio 5.02

1 I was supposed to open a student bank account today, but I forgot.
2 I was going to ask whether you could help me write a new CV.
3 I was going to advise you against going self-employed.
4 I was meant to email my application form, but I got distracted.
5 I'd love to own a business one day, but I'm not sure what yet.

Audio 5.03

Presenter: Now, according to a recent survey conducted by the Workers' Association, only two out of every five people achieve their childhood ambitions. But what's it like when you actually do? We took to the streets of Manchester to find out.
Mark: Hi, my name's Mark and I'm a criminal lawyer.
Presenter: And is that what you always wanted to do?
Mark: Er, yeah. Whenever anyone asked me the question 'What do you want to be when you grow up?' I would immediately say 'lawyer'. Who knows where I got that idea from at the age of ten – TV maybe? Anyway, I did what I'd planned to do, got my qualifications and experience working in different areas of law to see which I was most suited to, and I ended up as a criminal lawyer.
Presenter: And is it as exciting as they make it out to be on TV?
Mark: No, not really – it can be a real challenge. I couldn't think of doing anything else, though.
Amanda: I'm Amanda and I'm a professional footballer.
Presenter: And is that what you wanted to be when you were growing up?
Amanda: Yeah, I was desperate to play football for a living, but, to be honest, it wasn't all that common for women to make a career out of it. There just wasn't much money in the women's game. That didn't stop me dreaming about money, fame, or adoring fans though!

AUDIOSCRIPTS

Presenter: Ha! And is that what you've got now?
Amanda: Well, don't get me wrong, I love my sport, but unless you're amongst the very lucky few who play for a top women's team, you might as well put ideas of fame and fortune out of your mind! Most of the women in the team I play for have to do other jobs as well, so we don't have much time to train. Have I fulfilled my dream? Kind of, but it's not exactly what I was hoping for.
Chilemba: I'm Chilemba and I'm a drone operator.
Presenter: Really? That's a very unusual job.
Chilemba: Yeah. I wouldn't say that's what I was planning to get into as a kid, but I did always like remote-controlled toys and anything that could fly. So when I saw a job advertised, I went for it. People don't really get what I do. I think maybe they think I deliver parcels or something. But I actually do filming for a TV company. You know, those aerial shots you get over towns or inaccessible places round the planet. It's a dream come true.
Kiku: Hello, I'm Kiku and I'm an environmental policy maker.
Presenter: And I take it that wasn't your childhood ambition?
Kiku: Er, no! Like everyone else at that age, I wanted to be an astronaut or a firefighter or a film star. It's not that no one does those things any more but I think they've kind of fallen out of fashion when it comes to young people's aspirations today. Once I got to university, I realised that young people now are more likely to be set on working in big data or saving the planet and I'm no different. I love what I've ended up doing and I'm going to work my way up.
Presenter: Wow! Great to hear that you really can achieve your childhood ambitions.

Audio 5.04

Perhaps I don't need to give up on my hopes of becoming an astronaut just yet!

Audio 5.05

1   Male 1: I don't understand why you can't hear me – there seems to be a problem with the mute button.
    Female 1: I can't hear you! Can you type what's wrong in the chat box? … Oh, I see! Maybe it's the microphone on your laptop. Why don't you try using your headphones instead?
    Male 1: Can you hear me now?
    Female 1: Yes!
2   Female 2: Can you see that photo of us on our trip?
    Male 2: Nope! Have you shared it yet?
    Female 2: Yes … I've clicked on the 'share screen' button. … Hmm, I can't get it to work.
    Male 2: Hmm … that's odd. Maybe you could leave the meeting for a second or two and come back in. That might work.
3   Male 3: Hello …? Oh, that's annoying … I've got a horrible echo.
    Female 3: Perhaps you could try turning your volume down. It's worth a try because it sometimes gets rid of it.
    Male 3: … Hello? Oh, yes – thanks!

Audio 5.06

1 There seems to be a problem with the mute button.
2 Why don't you try using your headphones instead?
3 I've clicked on the 'share screen' button. Hmm, I can't get it to work.
4 Maybe you could leave the meeting for a second or two.
5 Perhaps you could try turning your volume down.
6 It's worth a try because it sometimes gets rid of it.

Audio 5.07

1 Perhaps you could log off and log in again?
2 You could try sending the link again.
3 It might be worth sharing your screen.
4 It sometimes helps if you turn your camera off.
5 That might work if you haven't already tried it.

Audio 5.08 and 5.09

Alfie: How's it going?
Sally: Well, we've got a load of jobs to do around the house today. There seems to be a problem with the washing machine. It's not emptying.
Alfie: Oh, dear. Maybe you could find a number for a plumber while I take a quick look. I doubt I'll be able to fix it, though.
Sally: Sure. There's something wrong with my bike brakes as well. I'll try replacing the brake pads. That might work because I'm sure they're pretty old now.
Alfie: Good idea. Actually, I can't get the games console working.
Sally: Why don't you try taking it to that repair guy?
Alfie: It might be worth a try…

Audio 5.10

Presenter: Traditionally, team-building activities – which seek to improve teamworking and collaboration in the workplace – have taken the form of away-days and in-house activities. These often involve physical challenges, such as adventure sports or competitive exercises like building a bridge or solving puzzles. Today, with an increasing number of employees working from home, employers have had to get more inventive about bringing teams together. Although many workers report greater job satisfaction from working at home, there is an increase in people feeling alone. Natural team-building opportunities which might have happened at breaktimes in the office or at the beginning and end of the day, have nearly all disappeared. Connecting with others is a huge part of working life, so companies that are creative when it comes to bringing teams together in a fun way are on to a winner. So, what kind of team-building activities can be done remotely? Let's hear from three managers who injected a bit of fun into their teams' lives.
Male 1: I really wanted to find a way to bring my team together, so I found a company that organised an online escape room activity. During the activity, small teams had to use virtual clues to solve a mystery and get out of the room before they got locked in. It was a race against time, with several teams competing to escape first. Everyone told me how much fun they'd had. I was really impressed. I would recommend the activity very highly!
Female 1: My team and I did a virtual travel challenge. Together, we had to complete a series of challenges to win enough credits to get us to the next destination and complete our round-the-world journey. We had to do things like perform a traditional dance or answer questions about well-known places. It required a lot of collaboration and creativity, and the time limit we were given to get back home increased the sense of fun and urgency.

AUDIOSCRIPTS

Male 2: We did a virtual murder mystery. We joined together as a team to investigate a crime. We got to interview suspects and rule them out one by one in order to catch the real killer. It was a bit harder than we'd expected, but that meant we really had to work together and communicate well in order to progress. We got the right answer in the end, which really boosted morale! We felt really positive afterwards!

Presenter: If you've got a great idea for a remote team building exercise, email us at the usual address and we'll mention the best ones later in the programme. But for now …

UNIT 6

Audio 6.01

1 I'm usually quite an impatient person, but in my work as a teacher, I'm very understanding.
2 Who disconnected my laptop? I was charging it for later.
3 I've rewritten this paragraph three times already and I'm tired of doing it now!
4 I have poor concentration, so working in an open-plan office is impractical for me.
5 I'm afraid this report is substandard and it will need to be revised.

Audio 6.02

1 She admitted taking the money.
2 He threatened to leave the project.
3 They asked me to move in with them.
4 He emphasised that he didn't blame me.
5 She suggested that I apply for the role.

Audio 6.03

Bea: So, people always seem to know whether they're an introvert or an extrovert when you ask them, but I don't think I'm either.
Oli: Well, maybe you're both!
Bea: What do you mean?
Oli: Well, apparently, people can be ambiverts or omniverts, too. That's what an article I read said, anyway.
Bea: OK … ?
Oli: So, according to the article, an ambivert is neither extroverted nor introverted. Their behaviour and energy levels are always somewhere in between. So, they're not an extrovert and they're not an introvert. That makes a lot of sense to me. I bet there are loads of ambiverts out there – probably more than there are true extroverts or true introverts to be honest.
Bea: Hmm, probably. What else did the article say about ambiverts?
Oli: It reported that they can adapt easily to lots of different situations. I'm not sure, but I guess that means you know when to talk and when not to, or something like that. Some professor argued that ambiverts are great salespeople for exactly this reason.
Bea: Interesting … They sound quite flexible.
Oli: I guess so.
Bea: So, what about omniverts, then?
Oli: They're people who can be both introvert and extrovert.
Bea: I don't follow.
Oli: Well, the article suggested that sometimes they behave like an extrovert and sometimes behave like an introvert. Like, one day they might do loads of social activities and be their extrovert self, and then they'll need downtime to recover and chill out – that's their introvert side. Oh, and I thought this was particularly fascinating: when there's a situation which demands too much of them or is overwhelming, omniverts are more likely to become more introverted. Strange, huh? And I suppose that after they've 'recharged their batteries', they'll need to be extrovert again and go out and party!
Bea: That definitely sounds more like me … I've got some really extrovert friends and some really introvert friends, and depending on how I'm feeling, I'll contact one group or another.
Oli: Exactly! So, you must be an omnivert.

Audio 6.04

Bea: What about you? Are you an extrovert, introvert, ambivert or omnivert?
Oli: I pretty sure I'm an ambivert. You know how when we're in class at uni, and our tutor has asked us to take part in a discussion?
Bea: Yes … You're a good listener but you'll speak up, too. So, that's your 'ambivertism'!
Oli: Right. And I can adapt to the situation. Whereas I've noticed that you behave depending on how you're feeling – I never know whether you're going to be quiet and thoughtful, or more chatty and outgoing.
Bea: You're absolutely right. Hey, can I borrow that article? I'd like to know more about what it claimed.
Oli: It's online – I'll email you the link.
Bea: I'd appreciate that.

Audio 6.05

Oli: The psychology of people is so interesting, isn't it?

Audio 6.06

1 A: So, I'm thinking about dropping out of uni. I always liked geography at school, but my grades are terrible. Maybe I should just get a job instead. What do you think?
  B: Well, I hope you don't take this the wrong way, but have you been working hard enough? I mean, you do seem to be going out a lot … Perhaps you should stick with it, but put a few more hours in. It would be a shame to stop halfway through the course.
2 A: Urgh, I'm sooooo tired! All I ever seem to do is work. Maybe I should look for a new job? What would you do?
  B: It's not your job, it's you. To be honest, I think you go to bed too late. Like, yesterday, you said you were up till two a.m. And you were at work at nine … I don't think you're really getting enough sleep. You should definitely go to bed earlier and try to get eight hours' sleep a night.
3 A: Oh, come on! I can't have lost my keys again. Where are they? Honestly, I can never find anything in this flat. Jacob's always moving things around. It's annoying.
  B: Look, don't take it personally, but you're always in such a rush that you just leave things around all over the place – no wonder you can't find them when you need them. If I were you, I'd get a little bowl to put your keys in.

Audio 6.07

1 Maybe I should just get a job instead. What do you think?
2 Well, I hope you don't take this the wrong way, but have you been working hard enough?
3 Perhaps you should stick with it but put a few more hours in.
4 Maybe I should look for a new job. What would you do?
5 To be honest, I think you go to bed too late.
6 You should definitely go to bed earlier and try to get eight hours' sleep a night.
7 Look, don't take it personally, but you're always in such a rush.
8 If I were you, I'd get a little bowl to put your keys in.

AUDIOSCRIPTS

Audio 6.08 and 6.09
1 Perhaps you should do more preparation before your interview.
2 Have you thought about buying some new clothes?
3 It might be a good idea to think about how your words affect people.
4 Maybe you should just ask her what she thinks.

Audio 6.10 and 6.11
Mark: Do you think I should buy this baseball cap?
Rob: Don't get me wrong but I think you might be a little old for baseball caps now …
Mark: Really?! So what would you get?
Rob: If you really want my advice, it's not a hat you should be worrying about …
Mark: What? What do you mean?
Rob: Well, you do dress a bit like a teenager. Maybe it's time to buy more grown-up clothes?
Mark: Hmmm … it might be a good idea to get a couple of shirts I suppose.
Rob: Yeah, that would be a good start. Why don't you ask the sales assistant for some advice?
Mark: Good idea. Excuse me … !

Audio 6.12
1 I really don't know what to do about finding a new job. Anyway, how are you?
2 So, I told her that I wouldn't be going back to that café any time soon!
3 As I say, I don't really like that kind of food, so why she'd made it when I'd told her that, I don't know.
4 I find TV so boring these days. Mind you, I did watch a good film last night.
5 OK, let's get started. Right, in front of you, you'll see several scientific instruments.

UNIT 7

Audio 7.01
1 You can't have been living here that long, surely!
2 Meiko must have known the questions in advance.
3 I couldn't have done the amount of training required anyway.
4 It must have been cold with the roof off like that.
5 They might have eaten before they came.

Audio 7.02
1 I always found driving a piece of cake, right from my first lesson.
2 Missing the concert was a blessing in disguise – I had an early night instead.
3 Icelandic death metal isn't my cup of tea, I'm afraid!
4 The grass isn't greener – I can tell you that for sure.
5 The funding fell through, so I had to go back to the drawing board.
6 Sandra missed the boat because she didn't apply in time.

Audio 7.03
1 I always had a talent for languages at school and did well in language exams. The primary school I went to as a child was a bit unusual because they taught us some basic French, unlike other schools in the area. I went on to do exams in French and German, and then at university, I took Italian as a minor subject in my first year alongside engineering. I did really well in Italian, too, but when it came to choosing what to concentrate on, I went full-time with my other subject. I wish I'd taken Italian as part of my degree now. I could've worked abroad in a country I love.

2 I've always had a passion for stories. I think it came from my parents reading me a bedtime story when I was tiny. My dad was brilliant at coming up with stories, too, and eventually, I started making up my own. I even did a story-telling course and went on to be a storyteller at festivals – for adults as well as kids. I thought about doing it professionally, but I wasn't convinced I'd get enough work. Now I've got a pretty dull office job and I often think I should've just gone for it, even if it hadn't worked out.

3 I'd probably have gained a qualification in speech therapy if I'd known the job existed – you know, helping people with speech difficulties to communicate better. I'm fascinated by communication, and that's why I did a degree in linguistics. Then I went on to teaching and have worked in the field of education ever since. I enjoy the job, but now and then I think 'If only I'd known about speech therapy sooner'. It seems such a worthwhile job – not that education isn't, of course.

Audio 7.04
1 There's no point in going over the whole story again.
2 You need to figure out what you want to do in life.
3 Remember to slow down when you're speaking so people can understand you.
4 Please don't go into all the details of what happened now – you can tell me later.
5 I left out some critical information in my interview.

Audio 7.05
Whether you've just graduated and are looking for a new job, or simply want to find something new, it's important to have a strong, professional online presence.
My name's Maya Kahn and I'm an experienced careers advisor. Today, I'm going to show you how to create the perfect online profile to help you secure that perfect job!

Audio 7.06
To begin with, you need to look at the platform where your profile will appear. These will often provide you with a sort of template, with different sections for you to fill in.
The first thing you might be asked to do is upload a current photo. This is optional, but a friendly-looking photo can make you look approachable and open to communication. Be careful not to use a photo showing you in a social setting where you may not appear professional.
You will be asked to provide contact details for potential employers. You must provide this information so that you don't miss out on networking opportunities.
The next step is organising your qualifications and work experience into a logical order. It's common to begin with the most recent thing you've done: so, your current job or most recent qualification. There may also be a section where you can include feedback from teachers or employers.
The final stage involves checking through what you've written, making sure you've missed nothing out, such as a particular talent or skill, and ensuring there are no typos or other mistakes. Then, you're ready to go!

Audio 7.07 and 7.08
Jo: So, what are you going to do this summer?
Tom: Well, I'd love to plan a walking trip like you did. But I've got no idea how to get started!
Jo: Well, to begin with, you'll need to decide where you're going!
Tom: Ha ha! True. Well, I'd like to go to the mountains, but I guess that means having to camp.
Jo: You can if you want. Or you could stay in a hostel near where you're walking.
Tom: OK, and once I've found somewhere, can I just turn up? Or do I need to book in advance?

75

AUDIOSCRIPTS

Jo: Well, I'd avoid just turning up because they might not have any rooms left.
Tom: OK. Any other advice?
Jo: It's essential that you tell someone where you're going each day and when you'll be back.
Tom: What, in case I get lost? But I'll have my phone.
Jo: Yeah, but you might not get a signal in the mountains. I'd recommend buying an actual map and compass, too.
Tom: Good idea. Thanks for the advice!

Audio 7.09

Presenter: Now, as a professional musician, when to retire can be a big decision. Most want to keep playing until they're physically unable. But that's not the case for this morning's guest, Michael Alfi. Until recently, Michael was one of the world's foremost violinists. He toured the globe, regularly playing to sell-out crowds. But just under a month ago, he decided to give it all up to try something new, and I for one, would like to know why.
So, Michael – why is it that you don't play anymore?

Michael: Well, the truth is – I just don't want to. In fact, I may never pick the instrument up again. I've done very well – though there's always more you can do. I think I'm now going to turn to another passion of mine – cricket. I'm still young enough to go professional. However, that's not the reason I quit the violin. I couldn't handle the stress of it all – the expectation to perform well every time.

Presenter: That's interesting. Was playing the violin something you used to want to do?

Michael: Well, this answer may be a little unexpected, but no. I grew up in a country that my parents had emigrated to. They didn't have much money, and struggled to get by. Once they realised I had talent – which a schoolteacher had identified – they really pushed me on. Although I wasn't all that interested, I picked it up quickly, and started winning competitions.

Presenter: Don't you think parents should encourage their children to do well?

Michael: Of course they should. But expectations were just too high in my case and that's not right for anyone. It could be that my parents never had the opportunity to do anything other than ordinary jobs. But, maybe they wanted to prove that, although they were immigrants, their family was just as good as those around them. I get it.

Presenter: How do they feel about you giving it all up?

Michael: You know, I actually don't think they're that bothered that I've decided to chase another dream. I think I've given them enough hints by now that it's not how I want to spend the rest of my life. Once they've got used to the idea, I know they'll support me in my new career, though I think they're a bit upset that I've stopped altogether.

Presenter: Do you think you might regret your decision in the future?

Michael: Never say never. I might pick it up again later in life – though only as a hobby. I'm closing the door on it right now, but I can't be certain I won't feel differently in a few years' time, whether or not I make it as a cricket player.

Presenter: What if your cricket career doesn't work out? How will you feel?

Michael: If it doesn't happen, it doesn't happen. However, I'll do everything I can to succeed. I might feel a bit sorry about it, but more than anything, I'll be glad I left the violin to see what I could do. What would I do next? Well, that's a tricky question. Coaching maybe? Whatever I decide, I'll give it one hundred percent!

UNIT 8

Audio 8.01

1 Having rented throughout his thirties, David was finally able to buy his own home.
2 Looking out of the window, Sasha realised how much she loved this place.
3 Having worked at the company for fifty years, she finally retired last month.
4 Thinking about their future, the couple started researching schools in the area.
5 Having lived in many different places, Kim finally decided to settle down.

Audio 8.02

1 As long as we leave home by seven-thirty, we won't be late.
2 Unless we take action now, the damage will be catastrophic.
3 Provided that endangered languages are taught, they will survive.
4 On condition that the loan is paid back in full, we're happy to approve the request.

Audio 8.03

Thank you. Now, I want to start off by telling you about a friend of mine called Nadim. Nadim is now sixteen years old, but when he first came to me, he was still in primary school. Although he had great social skills and enjoyed subjects like Maths and Science, Nadim struggled with reading and writing.
Over the next few years, we provided Nadim and his family with a lot of extra support and I'm pleased to say that he's now become much more confident of his literacy skills. Although things worked out for Nadim, sadly there are still thousands of children in the UK entering school with a similar issue, and today I want to explain how you can help address it.

Audio 8.04

The importance of child literacy cannot be overstated, and in today's presentation, I'm going to talk about why literacy is so crucial to children, and how it can be improved or gained later in life by those who missed out in childhood.
Firstly, what is literacy? In simple terms it's the ability to read and write. However, this varies across cultures. For example, in the UK, reading comprehension is an important part of literacy, but this may not be the case in places where people rarely read in print. Similarly, older generations may not be as 'literate' in digital media as younger people.
Unless people can read, they will struggle with many everyday tasks. For example, we need to read timetables and labels – such as instructions for taking medicine or cooking food. We also read signs, to help us get around. In the past, if we wanted to communicate with people, we made phone calls. These have been replaced by instant messaging. For example, appointments might be confirmed this way, and we make arrangements to see friends and family by text because it's quick and efficient. And this is fine. These are basic functions of reading and writing, but we need literacy for social purposes, too. We

AUDIOSCRIPTS

need to be able to understand current events and be able to communicate properly with other people. A high level of literacy enables us to do this better.

So, how can young people be supported from the earliest age when it comes to literacy? Reading bedtime stories to very young children is where the journey starts. Later, provided that they are able to read for themselves, they should be encouraged to access a wide variety of materials, such as the news, magazines, websites and novels.

But what about those who struggle with reading and writing? There are a variety of ways to help. If a child is falling behind their peers, early action will help. Choose books at the right level, and consider audiobooks which will still help them with comprehension. There are specialist apps that are accessible for children and children will enjoy the interaction.

Learning to read can be made fun. For example, teachers can ask children to describe an object using as many adjectives as they can, or they can read clues in a game to find treasure. They can get interested in writing short poems, or review a film they've seen. The opportunities are endless.

Of course, trips to the library are a great place to start and can be made with very young children. They can be an exciting weekly event, when children choose their own books and enjoy reading them with parents or guardians.

Finally, what about adult literacy? If someone had missed a lot of school through illness as a child, they would probably have fallen behind and struggled to catch up, for example. Adults can be encouraged in similar ways to children. Fortunately, today there is plenty of teaching material aimed at adults who've missed out.

Audio 8.05

In conclusion, by working together, we can tackle literacy problems head on.

Audio 8.06

A: I'd like to start off by saying that I completely agree that social media has killed the art of conversation.
This is true for three main reasons. Firstly, we no longer have to interact face to face with people who disagree with us. We can block or unfriend anyone with a different opinion, rather than engaging with them. As a result, we are no longer able to discuss our views in person with someone that we disagree with.
Secondly, whereas in the past we had to call or arrange to meet someone we hadn't spoken to in a long while, now we can just fire off a quick message online. It's easier, but it has clearly led to fewer meaningful interactions.
Finally, it can be difficult to express yourself online as everything relies on the text itself. All of that extra information, like body language and your tone of voice, has been removed. The impact of this is often miscommunication and confusion.
For these reasons, it's clear that social media has had a negative impact on our ability to have meaningful, face-to-face conversations.

B: With respect, I completely disagree with all three points. As far as I can see, it's up to the individual whether they interact with people that have different opinions. Social media isn't forcing you to block people. It's your choice, so if anything, it's *you* that's …

Audio 8.07

1 I'd like to start off by saying that I completely agree that social media has killed the art of conversation.
2 This is true for three main reasons. Firstly, we no longer have to interact face to face …
3 As a result, we are no longer able to discuss our views in person with someone that we disagree with.
4 It's easier, but it has clearly led to fewer meaningful interactions.
5 The impact of this is often miscommunication and confusion.

Audio 8.08

1 I'd like to start off by saying that I completely agree that social media has killed the art of conversation.
2 Firstly, we no longer have to interact face to face with people who disagree with us.
3 Secondly, whereas in the past we had to call or arrange to meet someone we hadn't spoken to in a long while, now we can just fire off a quick message online.

Audio 8.09

I'd like to start off by saying that I fully believe in small businesses making use of online platforms to promote their service or products. The evidence suggests that this can be a great way to reach a lot of people quickly. A good example of this is beauty products. By uploading regular photos and videos to the right platforms, you can reach huge numbers of people. The obvious impact of this is that sales will increase dramatically in a short space of time. The second point I'd like to make is that online marketing will save you money. This is true for two main reasons. Firstly, you won't have to pay as much in advertising, and secondly, you can do much of the work yourself.

ANSWER KEY

UNIT 1

Lesson 1A
VOCABULARY

1A **1** b **2** a **3** a **4** c **5** b **6** c

1B **1** argumentative
  2 rebellious
  3 cheerful
  4 outgoing
  5 ambitious
  6 adventurous
  7 curious
  8 stubborn

2 **1** helpful
  2 artistic
  3 talented
  4 emotional
  5 realistic
  6 likeable
  7 experienced

GRAMMAR

3A **1** been calling
  2 had
  3 been having
  4 visited
  5 been studying
  6 raised

3B **1** 've/have (always) been
  2 've/have been working
  3 've/have had
  4 has helped
  5 've/have been practising
  6 's/has been

3C **1** I've seen that new Wes Anderson film five times now.
  2 You've been working on that report all morning!
  3 Have you been anywhere interesting recently?
  4 Ben's never tried horse-riding because he's scared of horses!
  5 He's taken a year off to go travelling.
  6 I've been looking for you for the last half an hour!

PRONUNCIATION

4A **1** She's never been
  2 have you been
  3 he been
  4 I've been
  5 She's been

LISTENING

5A The correct order is: c, e, d, a, b.

5B **1** personality traits
  2 make important decisions
  3 a model
  4 fixed
  5 feed into

5C Explore and experiment, find out what you like doing and who you identify with.

WRITING

6A **1** adventurous
  2 risk-taker
  3 indoor activities
  4 music teacher
  5 curious
  6 extreme

6B Present perfect simple: I've actually changed, I've always been, I've taken up, I've changed, I've outgrown, I've changed, I've always had
Present perfect continuous: I've been channelling, I've been working

6C Sample answer: Have I changed as I've got older? I don't think my personality's all that different and it doesn't seem to change much in my work or in my personal life. I'm neither outgoing nor shy, though I can be more or less of those things depending on who I'm with.
I've had the same hobbies since I was a kid. I still love nothing more than dancing and playing music. Recently, I've taken up swimming, too, though I haven't been attending classes lately as I've injured my shoulder.
As for values, I think I've become more open-minded and judge other people less than I used to. I'd like to think people see me that way, too. I'm more likely to stand up for myself and others, as well.

Lesson 1B
VOCABULARY

1 **1** remember every detail
  2 short-term
  3 heart
  4 brought back memories
  5 childhood
  6 got

2A **1** c **2** b **3** f **4** e **5** a **6** d

2B **1** on the tip of my tongue
  2 rings a bell
  3 memory is playing tricks on me
  4 refresh my memory
  5 in one ear and out the other
  6 slipped my mind

PRONUNCIATION

3A **1** short-term memory
  2 perfect recall
  3 childhood memories

GRAMMAR

4A **1** to meet
  2 to set
  3 getting up
  4 going
  5 to have
  6 to lock

4B **1** to climb
  2 to improve
  3 setting off
  4 to make sure
  5 having
  6 to reach

ANSWER KEY

READING

5A 2, 3, 5, 6

5B 1 help us recall past events, learn from our mistakes, creating our identities
2 we wish that what we are saying is true, or we want our listener to think in a particular way …, we might want to make them laugh or feel sorry for us
3 false memories
4 the 'audience-tuning' effect
5 fill in the gaps

5C 1 b 2 c 3 b

Lesson 1C
VOCABULARY

1A 1 about
2 of
3 of
4 by
5 on
6 into
7 of
8 about

1B 1 passionate about
2 nervous about
3 keen on
4 terrified of
5 fed up of
6 really into

HOW TO …

2A Going on holiday / going backpacking together; Yes, they do.

2B 1 my kind of thing
2 not a big fan of
3 How about if we
4 I'd love to
5 don't want to
6 sound like a plan

PRONUNCIATION

3A and **3B**
1 I'm quite <u>fond</u> of boat trips, actually. They're a great way to see the city.
2 The kids aren't <u>keen</u> on trying unusual foods.
3 Dan's <u>ter</u>rified of driving in foreign countries and so am I!
4 I'm not <u>real</u>ly into visiting museums. I find a lot of them really boring.
5 I always feel <u>ner</u>vous about getting lost when I'm in a new city.
6 Katie's quite <u>pass</u>ionate about culture and the arts.

SPEAKING

4A 1 e 2 c 3 d 4 f 5 b 6 a

Lesson 1D
GRAMMAR

1A 1 d 2 a 3 f 4 e 5 b 6 c

1B 1 confident with friends, intimidated by people at work
2 to see you, too much work to do
3 meeting new people, not very sociable
4 my parents, walking home
5 mowed the lawn, cleaned the house
6 self-esteem, very confident

LISTENING

2A 1 e 2 c 3 b 4 a 5 d

2B 1 perfect combination
2 (usually) punctual
3 educational context
4 shy
5 feelings
6 negative emotions

2C To sum up, everyone has all five traits to a greater or lesser degree!

UNIT 2

Lesson 2A
VOCABULARY

1 1 Smart
2 analyse
3 remotely
4 predicted
5 findings
6 Researchers
7 tech industry
8 virtual reality

2 1 b 2 a 3 c 4 a 5 c 6 b

GRAMMAR

3A 1 definitely won't
2 unlikely
3 certain to
4 due to
5 may not
6 could

3B 1 is unlikely to
2 is going to
3 I'll ever attend / I'd ever attend
4 is certain to / will certainly
5 due to hand in
6 might find

PRONUNCIATION

4A 1 certain to
2 due to
3 going to
4 unlikely to
5 is going to
6 likely to

READING

5A 1 a 2 b 3 b 4 a 5 a 6 b

5B 1 T
2 T
3 T
4 F (She is amazed by it.)
5 F (She has not presented at a conference yet.)
6 T

Lesson 2B
VOCABULARY

1A 1 b 2 f 3 a 4 c 5 e 6 d

1B 1 woodland
2 river bank
3 open spaces
4 tracks
5 scenery
6 sunlight

ANSWER KEY

GRAMMAR

2A 1 few
2 No
3 minority
4 little
5 a handful of
6 a few

2B 1 a handful of
2 A few
3 Every/Each
4 no / not any
5 lack
6 little
7 deal
8 few

PRONUNCIATION

3A 1 There's a lack‿of attractive green spaces in my town.
2 Only a handful‿of people I know live in the countryside.
3 I spend a good‿deal‿of my time outdoors.
4 Several‿of‿the beaches nearby are quite good.
5 Young people who like gardening are‿in‿a minority.

LISTENING

4A c

4B a 3 b 2 c 1 d 2 e 3 f 1

4C 1 T
2 F (She wasn't sure whether it was because of the garden or getting away from her desk.)
3 T
4 F (He became interested over time.)
5 T
6 T
7 F (She has a lot of new knowledge about plants.)

4D Now I grow all sorts of things on my balcony overlooking the sea.

WRITING

5A c

5B 1 Despite
2 While/Although
3 Although/While
4 However
5 However
6 despite

5C 1 Although ~~despite~~ I love living in the city, …
2 However, ~~Although~~ I'm starting to find it a little small.
3 Although/While ~~Despite~~ many people I know prefer renting, …
4 Although/While ~~However~~ there can be a great sense of community in villages …
5 Despite ~~Although~~ the fact that public transport is so good in the city,
6 However, ~~Despite~~ I'll admit it can be boring at times.

5E Sample answer:
Some people prefer to spend most of their time indoors, while others prefer to be outdoors. So, which is most beneficial for our well-being?
Let's first consider mental well-being. Although there's much to be said for snuggling down to binge-watch the latest hit TV series, or talking about our worries over coffee with friends, it's just as important to get mood-boosting fresh air in our lungs and sunlight on our faces.
Despite warnings, when it comes to physical well-being, many of us still don't get moving as much as we should. However, it isn't difficult to build in a few minutes' walk a day, even if sports aren't our thing. Of course, the more exercise we do, the healthier our bodies become.
While indoor and outdoor activities are both advantageous for our well-being, I believe it is a combination of the two that benefits us most.

Lesson 2C

VOCABULARY

1 1 unique
2 ordinary
3 harsh
4 rewarding
5 exhausting
6 tedious
7 modest

HOW TO …

2A what living on a tiny/small island is like; how going to live on the mainland will affect them; whether anyone will be living in the area in 100 years' time

2B 1 c 2 h 3 a 4 e 5 g 6 b 7 f 8 d

PRONUNCIATION

3 1 way
2 fact
3 not
4 clearly
5 bound

SPEAKING

4A and **4B**
1 imagine
2 impression
3 fact
4 way
5 sure
6 bound

Lesson 2D

VOCABULARY

1 1 finest
2 magnificent
3 mighty
4 precious
5 finest
6 astonishing

READING

2A 1 Yes
2 No (only in theory)

ANSWER KEY

2B
1. incredible
2. (our) mistakes
3. space-time
4. face creams
5. (mathematical) calculations
6. laws of physics
7. dark matter
8. wormholes

2C b

REVIEW 1–2
GRAMMAR
1
1. been learning
2. emailed
3. been
4. had
5. been working

2
1. to repair
2. to save
3. to go
4. to get
5. going
6. to say
7. to retrain
8. to do
9. seeing

3 Suggested answers
1. Whereas/While/Whilst I enjoy writing stories, I don't have a brilliant imagination.
2. While/Whilst I'm actually quite shy, I love performing on stage.
3. Whereas/While/Whilst I can organise other people, I can't organise myself.
4. Whereas/While/Whilst I'm happy to listen to people's problems, I don't like giving advice. / I'm happy to listen to people's problems, whereas/while/whilst I don't like giving advice.
5. Whereas/While/Whilst I've never enjoyed playing football, I've always enjoyed watching it. / I've never enjoyed playing football, whereas/while/whilst I've always enjoyed watching it.

4
1. to leave
2. going to happen
3. might not be
4. won't enjoy
5. will be able
6. will also be
7. won't need
8. be able
9. to meet
10. will give

5
1. a little
2. lack of
3. aren't any
4. majority
5. Very few

VOCABULARY
6
1. rebellious
2. argumentative
3. curious
4. adventurous
5. stubborn

7
1. experienced
2. optimistic
3. reliable
4. emotional
5. practical

8
1. recall
2. detail
3. memory
4. short-term
5. by heart

9
1. rings a bell
2. go in one ear and out the other
3. playing tricks on me
4. on the tip of my tongue
5. refresh my memory

10
1. up
2. of
3. into
4. about
5. on

11 1 a 2 c 3 b 4 a 5 c

12
1. research
2. predicted
3. analysis
4. researcher
5. scientific
6. remotely

13
1. sunlight
2. river bank
3. deserted
4. woodland
5. scenery

14
1. tedious
2. unique
3. modest
4. harsh
5. rewarding

15 1 a 2 b 3 a 4 a 5 b

UNIT 3
Lesson 3A
VOCABULARY
1
1. attending
2. line-up
3. acts
4. atmosphere
5. organisers
6. venue
7. attracts
8. festival-goers

2
1. footprint
2. resources
3. recycling
4. emissions
5. renewable
6. power

GRAMMAR
3A 1 c 2 a 3 c 4 b

3B sentences 1 and 3

81

ANSWER KEY

PRONUNCIATION

4A 1 Glastonbury Festival, <u>which has been running since 1970</u>, attracts over 200,000 visitors.
2 The band, <u>who had never played to such a large crowd before</u>, felt very nervous.
3 The headline act, <u>which will perform this evening, is expected to draw a huge crowd</u>.
4 Billie Eilish, <u>who has sold over 5 million records worldwide, will be on stage at nine</u>.
5 The orchestra, <u>which is bigger than ever</u>, will play on the Sticks stage this afternoon.
6 Woodstock, <u>which took place over three days in 1969</u>, was a turning point in music.

READING

5A green festivals, product quality, renewable energy, sustainable products, transport

5B 1 environmental policies
2 refill stations
3 go plastic-free
4 wind it up

WRITING

6A 1 to ask them to clean up after the festival

6B 1 f 2 a 3 e 4 b 5 c 6 d

6D See Ex 6A for a sample answer.

7A Sample answer:
In most towns and cities, people pay taxes and local governments use these taxes to maintain the local environment. While it would be good for people to look after their local environment, it would not work in practice.
The first reason is most people do not have time to tidy public gardens or clean up litter from the streets. People lead busy lives and do not have time for additional duties.
Also, some of these duties require skills or knowledge that most people do not have. Take looking after local woodland, for example. Most people would be unable to do that well.
Although people would probably look after their environment better if they had to do it themselves, I believe it is better for local governments to do this, by employing the right people with the right skills.

Lesson 3B

VOCABULARY

1A 1 b 2 a 3 c 4 c 5 a

1B 1 carry on
2 fall back on
3 came up with
4 put you off
5 ended up
6 put up with

2 1 speak up
2 get your message across
3 spell out
4 coming back to
5 bring up
6 came across
7 pointed out that
8 move on from

GRAMMAR

3A 1 d 2 a 3 h 4 b 5 f 6 g 7 e 8 c

3B 1 b 2 c 3 a 4 c

PRONUNCIATION

4A 1 What <u>I</u> like watching are the <u>less</u> well-<u>known acts</u>.
2 It was <u>Max</u> who left the car unlocked, <u>not me</u>.
3 What sounds better to <u>me</u> is finishing on a <u>minor chord</u>.
4 It's <u>you</u> who likes Italian <u>opera</u> – <u>that's</u> why I got the <u>tickets</u>!

LISTENING

5A D, A, E, B, C

5B 1 F (She got confused.)
2 T
3 T
4 F (They had to leave it until the interval.)
5 F (Alex would have understood if they had.)
6 T

5C 1 disaster
2 thousand
3 shaking
4 worst
5 fright
6 forever

5D It was still a relief to get off stage at the end of the night.

Lesson 3C

VOCABULARY

1A 1 based
2 cast
3 set
4 scenes
5 ending
6 twist
7 costumes
8 soundtrack

1B 1 subtitles
2 set
3 twist
4 cast
5 scene
6 based

HOW TO …

2A and stuff, bits, something like that, sort of, that kind of thing

2B 1 c 2 e 3 a 4 b 5 d

PRONUNCIATION

3A 1 getting caught up
2 sort of
3 based on
4 something like that

SPEAKING

4A 1 about
2 bit
3 and
4 of
5 or

ANSWER KEY

Lesson 3D
GRAMMAR
1A 1 didn't
2 don't
3 did
4 do
5 Do
6 did

1B 1 do
2 doesn't
3 did
4 did
5 don't
6 do
7 do
8 does

LISTENING
2A 1 jazz (music)
2 a jazz musician
3 a music critic

2B 1 c 2 b 3 a

2C 1 improvise / make music up
2 uncomfortable
3 technique
4 messy and noisy
5 interesting history
6 good introduction

2D All right, well I think it's time we listened to some, don't you?

UNIT 4

Lesson 4A
VOCABULARY
1 1 keep/stay
2 cut
3 expand
4 stay/keep
5 doing
6 did
7 worked
8 transformed
9 vary
10 keep

2A illness: allergies, asthma, food poisoning, run-down
treatment: antibiotics, first aid, medication, vaccine

2B 1 food poisoning
2 allergies
3 first aid
4 antibiotics/medication
5 vaccines/medication/antibiotics
6 run-down

GRAMMAR
3A 1 a 2 a 3 c 4 b

3B 1 have been
2 be celebrating
3 be having
4 be setting up
5 be going
6 have improved
7 have done
8 be writing

PRONUNCIATION
4A 1 I'll have finished
2 I'll have cut out
3 we'll have bought
4 we'll have eaten
5 you'll have graduated

READING
5A b

5B 1 T 2 F 3 T 4 F 5 F 6 T

5C 1 cell damage
2 (their) (hard-earned) cash
3 (another/a) marketing trick
4 ice cream

Lesson 4B
VOCABULARY
1A 1 exhausted
2 oversleep
3 dropping off
4 nightmare
5 snore
6 keep
7 sleeper
8 deep

1B 1 a 2 a 3 b 4 a 5 b 6 c

GRAMMAR
2A 1 d 2 a 3 e 4 c 5 b

2 1 is suggested/has been suggested
2 is (generally) accepted
3 is (also) suspected
4 was (once) assumed
5 is now not/is not now considered
6 is defined/has been defined
7 is (more easily) understood
8 is observed/has been observed
9 was noticed
10 wasn't/hasn't been discovered

PRONUNCIATION
3B 1 It was <u>thought</u> that <u>eating cheese</u> before <u>bedtime</u> gives you <u>nightmares</u>.
2 It's been <u>suggested</u> that <u>using</u> your <u>phone</u> in <u>bed</u> makes it <u>harder</u> to <u>drop off</u>.
3 It's <u>believed</u> that up to <u>fifteen percent</u> of the <u>population</u> are <u>sleepwalkers</u>.
4 It's <u>estimated</u> that <u>most</u> people sleep for <u>fewer</u> than <u>seven hours</u> a <u>night</u>.

LISTENING
4A a phone-in show

4B 1 c 2 a 3 c 4 c 5 b

4C Thanks to all of our callers for their advice.

WRITING
5A nightmares, sleep positions, lack of sleep, sleep and disability, dreams, sleep behaviour and conditions

5B 1 a 2 d 3 e 4 c 5 b

83

ANSWER KEY

5D Sample answer:
Some people fall asleep in seconds and wake up full of energy the next morning. Others take hours to get to sleep, wake up during the night and struggle to wake up the next day. Me? I'm a combination of the two. It's quite common for me, when I'm tired, to drop off within seconds. I can fall asleep on the sofa, on the train and even on my balcony. But at night, I can wake up an hour or two before my alarm goes off and then not get back to sleep.
So, what do I do? I try to relax, but my mind usually has other ideas. I try to focus on my breathing, but for some reason that just makes me feel anxious. I try every sleep position possible, but I can never quite find the right one. In the end, I usually just get up and start my day. I feel exhausted, but I can always have a nap later.

Lesson 4C
VOCABULARY
1 1 stamina
   2 aerobic
   3 Strength
   4 low-impact
   5 moderate
   6 High-impact

2 1 challenge
   2 encouragement
   3 incentive
   4 benefit
   5 discipline
   6 confidence

HOW TO …
3A Different kinds of exercise.
3B 1 PA 2 A 3 D 4 A 5 A 6 A

PRONUNCIATION
4A The main stress is on *point* in all three sentences.

SPEAKING
5A 1 couldn't agree
   2 you mean
   3 point
   4 disagree
   5 your point
   6 other hand

Lesson 4D
VOCABULARY
1 1 Time is running out
   2 just in time
   3 window of opportunity
   4 not a moment too soon
   5 is still under threat
   6 It's time to move on from
   7 under threat
   8 time

READING
2A to provide a balanced argument
2B 1 T 2 T 3 F 4 T 5 T 6 F 7 T 8 F

REVIEW 3–4
GRAMMAR
1 1 the theatre where Nick
   2 the girl we met at
   3 the guy whose car
   4 which opened last year
   5 the hotel we stayed

2 1 b 2 d 3 f 4 e 5 a 6 c

3 1 do
   2 did
   3 do
   4 don't
   5 does
   6 did
   7 does

4 1 be hearing
   2 will have got used to
   3 have fallen
   4 will have shrunk
   5 will have risen
   6 will have increased
   7 will have started
   8 will have done

5 1 a 2 c 3 b 4 c

VOCABULARY
6 1 line-up
   2 atmosphere
   3 organisers
   4 attended
   5 attracting
   6 festival-goers
   7 act
   8 venue

7 1 footprint
   2 recycling
   3 emissions
   4 resources
   5 power

8 1 come up with
   2 fall back on
   3 live up to
   4 messed up (all my lines) / messed (all my lines) up
   5 putting (me off)

9 1 across
   2 on to
   3 up
   4 back
   5 out

10 1 ending
   2 costumes
   3 soundtrack
   4 based on
   5 twist

ANSWER KEY

11
1. transform
2. sedentary
3. regular
4. stay
5. long
6. expand
7. vary
8. cut down
9. Keep
10. keep up

12
1. allergies
2. food poisoning
3. asthma
4. antibiotics
5. medication

13 1 b 2 a 3 b 4 a 5 c 6 a

14
1. vigourous
2. moderate
3. stamina
4. aerobic
5. flexibility

15
1. incentive
2. motivation
3. confidence
4. discipline
5. challenge

16
1. future
2. time
3. moment
4. opportunity
5. Time

UNIT 5

Lesson 5A

VOCABULARY

1A
1. By the time
2. Up to that point
3. just moments earlier
4. for ages / for a while
5. for a while / for ages
6. In no time

1B
1. for a while
2. just moments earlier
3. By the time
4. for ages
5. Up to that point
6. in no time

GRAMMAR

2A 1 c 2 a 3 b 4 b

2B
1. had introduced
2. 'd never seen
3. 'd been working
4. 'd been preparing
5. 'd forgotten
6. 'd spent
7. 'd already reduced
8. 'd been looking forward to
9. 'd always planned

PRONUNCIATION

3A
1. 'd been waiting
2. 'd been looking
3. hadn't been swimming
4. Had he been climbing
5. He'd been standing
6. 'd been asking

READING

4A and **B** Students' own answers.

4C
1. Elliott
2. Alex
3. Jitka
4. Alonzo
5. Elliott
6. Alex
7. Alonzo
8. Jitka

Lesson 5B

VOCABULARY

1A
1. reinventing
2. started out
3. switched
4. an entrepreneur
5. set up
6. advance

1B
1. reinvented
2. started out
3. part-time
4. retraining
5. Switching
6. advancing
7. setting up
8. entrepreneur

2
1. agriculture
2. social work
3. research
4. construction
5. journalism
6. Medicine
7. consultancy
8. publishing
9. Banking
10. accountancy

GRAMMAR

3
1. was hoping
2. had arranged
3. was planning
4. was considering
5. had finally decided
6. had always intended

PRONUNCIATION

4A
1. to‿open
2. to‿ask
3. to‿advise
4. to‿email
5. to‿own

LISTENING

5A Amanda

5B 1 T 2 F 3 T 4 F 5 F 6 T 7 F 8 T

5C Perhaps I don't need to give up on my hopes of becoming an astronaut just yet!

85

ANSWER KEY

WRITING

6A
1. recommended
2. purpose
3. slight
4. conclude
5. outlines
6. appears

6B in favour

6D Sample answer:

Remote-working vs office-based roles

Introduction
This report looks at remote-working and considers whether it is more or less effective than working in an office.

Background
For decades, employees have worked in offices alongside their colleagues. However, in recent years, remote-working has become much more popular due to the availability of new software.

Main issues
Remote-working has many benefits. For employees, it reduces commuting time, which means more free time and a better work-life balance. They may feel their environment is less competitive, too. All of these things make employees feel happier. It seems that younger employees in particular like their working environment to be flexible. For companies, remote-working reduces their carbon footprint and their staff work harder and stay longer at the company.

Conclusion
To conclude, remote-working has many benefits for employees and employers. It improves employees' health and happiness, which makes them more productive. I therefore recommend that this company switch from office-based roles to remote-working. However, I suggest that the company provides employees with computer and software support.

Lesson 5C

VOCABULARY

1A 1 b 2 a 3 c 4 a 5 c

1B
1. delays
2. 're frozen
3. a link
4. get into
5. host
6. on mute

HOW TO …

2A
1. problem: microphone not working; solution: use headphones
2. problem: can't share screen; solution: leave meeting for a short time
3. problem: there's an echo; solution: turn volume down

2B
1. seems to be
2. don't you try
3. to work
4. Maybe you could
5. could try
6. worth a

PRONUNCIATION

3A Speakers 2, 3 and 5 feel certain about what they are saying.

SPEAKING

4A and B

Alfie: How's it going?
Sally: Well, we've got a load of jobs to do around the house today. There seems to be a problem with the washing machine. It's not emptying.
Alfie: Oh, dear. Maybe you could find a number for a plumber while I take a quick look? I doubt I'll be able to fix it, though.
Sally: Sure. There's something wrong with my bike brakes as well. I'll try replacing the brake pads. That might work because I'm sure they're pretty old now.
Alfie: Good idea. Actually, I can't get the games console working.
Sally: Why don't you try taking it to that repair guy?
Alfie: It might be worth a try …

Lesson 5D

GRAMMAR

1A
1. which
2. who
3. where
4. when
5. whose
6. which

1B
1. which
2. who
3. where
4. whose
5. when
6. which

LISTENING

2A
1. an online escape room
2. a virtual travel challenge
3. a virtual murder mystery

2B 1 b 2 b 3 a 4 c 5 b 6 a

UNIT 6

Lesson 6A

VOCABULARY

1A
1. substandard, misunderstood
2. redo, unnecessary,
3. disconnect, impractical

1B
1. im
2. re
3. un
4. mis
5. un
6. im
7. re

PRONUNCIATION

2B
1. im<u>pa</u>tient
2. discon<u>nec</u>ted
3. re<u>wri</u>tten
4. im<u>prac</u>tical
5. sub<u>stan</u>dard

86

ANSWER KEY

GRAMMAR

3A 1 cutting
    2 isn't
    3 to stay
    4 leave
    5 to be done
    6 to take

3B 1 needs to be cut / needs cutting
    2 is not permitted
    3 is not allowed
    4 needs looking at / needs to be looked at
    5 is not forbidden
    6 is not allowed
    7 allowed; to stay
    8 permits

READING

4A c

4B 1 doing something you really enjoy and are fairly good at
    2 conversation, noises and other activity around them
    3 being more efficient
    4 peace of mind
    5 distractions

WRITING

5A A is the better set of notes.

5B Sample answer:
    Benefits
    Increased attention, learning, developing skills, better productivity & creativity, de-stressing, motivation, happiness.
    Characteristics of flow
    Activity needs to:
    • be rewarding
    • have achievable goals
    • make you feel in control
    • give you feedback straightaway
    • give you peace of mind
    Not all are needed at the same time.
    When flow happens
    Many areas of life, e.g. creative hobbies, sports, work, education.
    Need clear goals, few distractions, challenge. Must be enjoyable.
    How
    Practise. Increase level of challenge and skill.

Lesson 6B

VOCABULARY

1A 1 suggested
    2 admitted
    3 questioned
    4 refused
    5 boasted
    6 claimed

1B 1 suggested (that)
    2 claimed (that)
    3 to do
    4 doing
    5 criticised
    6 for being

PRONUNCIATION

2A 1 admitted
    2 threatened
    3 asked
    4 emphasised
    5 suggested

2B 1 ad<u>mit</u>ted
    2 <u>threat</u>ened
    3 a<u>sk</u>ed
    4 <u>empha</u>sised
    5 sugg<u>est</u>ed

GRAMMAR

3A 1 b 2 c 3 b 4 c

3B 1 advised, to take
    2 ordered, to stop
    3 asked, to rearrange
    4 instructed, to come
    5 asked, to remind
    6 advised, not to make

LISTENING

4A 1 c 2 b 3 a 4 c 5 a

4B 1 F 2 O 3 O 4 F 5 O

4C a

4D The psychology of people is so interesting, isn't it?

Lesson 6C

VOCABULARY

1A get: advice, involved, it wrong, something off your chest, the message, through to
    take: advice, it personally, your mind off

1B 1 get something off
    2 get the
    3 take it
    4 it wrong
    5 take your mind
    6 get through to
    7 Take
    8 get

HOW TO …

2A 1 someone is trying to make a decision
    2 someone is not getting enough sleep
    3 someone keeps losing things

2B 1 do you think
    2 you don't take this the wrong way
    3 Perhaps you should
    4 would you do
    5 To be honest
    6 should definitely
    7 take it personally
    8 I were you

PRONUNCIATION

3A 1 a 2 b 3 a 4 a

4A 1 should
    2 get
    3 would
    4 want
    5 might
    6 don't

ANSWER KEY

Lesson 6D
VOCABULARY
1A 1 Anyway
    2 So
    3 As I say
    4 Mind you
    5 OK, Right

1B d, b, e, c, a

READING
2A 1 f 2 e 3 a 4 c
2B 1 NM
    2 T
    3 T
    4 T
    5 F (We usually grow out of lying.)
    6 NM
    7 F (It is a complex process.)
    8 T

REVIEW 5–6
GRAMMAR
1 1 had been rushing
   2 had never been
   3 had been raining
   4 had been living
   5 had already seen
   6 had known

2 1 was planning
   2 take
   3 finish
   4 to get
   5 was meant
   6 was hoping
   7 becoming
   8 going

3 1 a 2 c 3 c 4 c 5 b

4 1 needed cleaning
   2 weren't allowed
   3 is (no longer) permitted
   4 was forbidden
   5 couldn't eat
   6 had to

5 1 ordered us/them to sit down
   2 advised me to ask the chemist for
   3 asked me to pass her / asked if/whether I could pass her
   4 told me to turn off the laptop when I'd finished
   5 requested some further information

VOCABULARY
6 1 by the time
   2 up to that point
   3 just moments earlier
   4 for ages
   5 for a while
   6 in no time

7 1 journalism
   2 banking
   3 publishing
   4 reinvented
   5 research
   6 set up

8 1 on mute
   2 frozen
   3 get into
   4 host
   5 delay
   6 link

9 1 impatient
   2 misread
   3 subheading
   4 dishonest
   5 redo
   6 unrealistic

10 1 denied
    2 insisted
    3 remind
    4 accused
    5 apologise
    6 refused

11 1 get
    2 take
    3 got
    4 taken
    5 get
    6 taking
    7 get
    8 get

12 f, g, a, c, b, e, d

UNIT 7

Lesson 7A
VOCABULARY
1 1 year-old
   2 respected
   3 famous
   4 lasting
   5 hand
   6 consuming
   7 changing
   8 consuming

2 1 b 2 a 3 c 4 a 5 b

GRAMMAR
3A 1 b 2 a 3 c 4 a

3B 1 couldn't have got
    2 couldn't/can't have happened
    3 couldn't/can't have had
    4 must have been
    5 could have had
    6 can't have been
    7 must have made

PRONUNCIATION
4A 1 can't have
    2 must have
    3 couldn't have
    4 must have
    5 might have

READING
5A brain injury, illness/dementia, savant syndrome

5B 1 g 2 b 3 e 4 a 5 f 6 c

88

ANSWER KEY

Lesson 7B
VOCABULARY
1A 1 a piece of cake
2 miss the boat
3 a blessing in disguise
4 the grass is always greener on the other side
5 back to the drawing board
6 not be someone's cup of tea

1B 1 b 2 a 3 a 4 a 5 c 6 b

PRONUNCIATION
2A 1 a piece of cake
2 a blessing in disguise
3 isn't my cup of tea
4 The grass isn't greener
5 go back to the drawing board
6 missed the boat

GRAMMAR
3A 1 I'd had
2 we lived
3 should have
4 would
5 I had
6 shouldn't have

3B 1 hadn't tried
2 had worked
3 would have
4 have spoken
5 hadn't crashed
6 hadn't eaten

LISTENING
4A 1 b 2 c 3 a

4B 1 b, a, c
2 a, c, b
3 c, b, a

WRITING
5B b

5C 1 b 2 a 3 d 4 f 5 e 6 c

5E Sample answer:
The grass isn't greener on the other side
I'm not sure why, but we always seem to think that the grass is greener elsewhere. The truth is that often it isn't, and we need to be happier with what we have. Last year, I met someone in the same industry as me. From her social media photos, her company seemed so much better, cooler and more fun than mine. So, I applied for a job there, and I got it!
But on my first day, I knew I shouldn't have changed jobs. The office wasn't as nice as it looked in the photos, and the staff didn't look quite as happy. The boss wasn't very nice either. I stayed there two weeks before I was completely sure that the grass had been greener in my old job. I begged my old boss to take me back. Luckily, she did.

Lesson 7C
VOCABULARY
1A 1 over/through
2 down
3 out
4 down
5 into
6 across
7 through
8 out

1B 1 c 2 a 3 a 4 c 5 b 6 b

PRONUNCIATION
2 1 going <u>over</u>
2 figure <u>out</u>
3 slow <u>down</u>
4 go <u>into</u>
5 left <u>out</u>

HOW TO …
3A a careers advisor; a professional online profile

3B b, f, c, e, a, d

3C 1 To begin with
2 This is optional
3 Be careful not to
4 The next step is
5 The final stage involves

SPEAKING
4A 1 begin
2 if
3 once
4 avoid
5 essential
6 recommend

Lesson 7D
GRAMMAR
1A 1 However
2 though
3 one, other
4 Through
5 though
6 however

1B 1 (al)though
2 However
3 On the other hand/(Al)Though
4 (Al)Though
5 On the one hand
6 on the other hand

LISTENING
2A 1 c 2 b 3 a 4 c 5 b 6 a

2B and **2C**
1 T 2 T 3 F 4 F 5 F 6 T

UNIT 8

Lesson 8A
VOCABULARY
1 1 gone
2 have
3 make
4 have
5 made
6 goes

89

ANSWER KEY

2
1. condition
2. spacious
3. fashionable
4. stylish
5. character
6. elegant

GRAMMAR

3A
1. Having worked
2. Having finished
3. Sitting
4. Not having completed
5. Opening

3B
1. Having cleaned
2. Having finished
3. Panicking
4. Having promised
5. Having left

PRONUNCIATION

4A
1. Having rented throughout his thirties
2. Looking out of the window
3. Having worked at the company for fifty years
4. Thinking about their future
5. Having lived in many different places

READING

5A sense of community

5B for: cheaper, you get more for your money, better for your mental health, access to nature
against: lack of (local job) opportunities, lack of nightlife, poor public transport, money saved on rent often goes on a train ticket, long commutes into the city, too quiet/lack of cultural amenities

WRITING

6A an estate/property agent

6B I would like to apply for the role of ….. as advertised; I am experienced in; I would now like to take the next step; I believe I would be suited to this role; good knowledge of

6D Sample answer:
Dear Sir or Madam,
I am a recent business graduate looking to start an exciting career at an estate agency. I am writing to apply for the position of trainee sales negotiator at your company.
I graduated from the University of Lancaster in June. Since then, I have been working at the office of estate agents Bewster & Barrett as an assistant to one of the sales agents. My role involves calling or emailing clients to inform them of new properties they may be interested in, and showing them around these properties.
I believe in good customer service and communication. I feel strongly that if you listen carefully to your clients and your colleagues, you can find exactly what your clients are looking for. While I do not have direct sales experience myself, I have been observing the agents at my company and I am keen to learn more.
Attached is my CV which will provide you with additional information about my qualifications and work experience. I have always worked part-time alongside my studies and have demonstrated a high level of professionalism in those jobs. I can provide references to confirm this. I can also be available for a job interview at your convenience.
I look forward to hearing from you.
Your sincerely,
Clara Coleman

Lesson 8B
VOCABULARY

1A
1. homelessness
2. endangered languages
3. justice
4. overcrowding
5. civil rights
6. global warming
7. literacy
8. unemployment
9. poverty
10. housing

1B
1. homelessness
2. unemployment
3. overcrowding
4. poverty
5. justice

GRAMMAR

2A 1 e 2 b 3 f 4 a 5 c 6 d

2B
1. Unless
2. if not
3. long as
4. Providing
5. condition

2C
1. Providing that
2. hadn't
3. may not have been
4. Unless
5. if

PRONUNCIATION

3A
1. thirty
2. now
3. taught
4. full

LISTENING

4A c

4B
1. signs
2. arrangements / appointments
3. Social
4. bedtime stories / audiobooks
5. library
6. illness

4C
1. T
2. T
3. F (She says they're 'quick and efficient' and 'basic functions of reading and writing'.)
4. F (She says they should be 'encouraged to access a wide variety of materials, including websites.')
5. T
6. T

4D In conclusion, by working together, we can tackle literacy problems head on.

ANSWER KEY

Lesson 8C
VOCABULARY
1A 1 On the whole
2 In order to
3 by far
4 at the same time
5 In fact
6 out of control

1B 1 in order to
2 In fact
3 at least
4 On the whole
5 At the same time
6 by far
7 out of control

HOW TO …
2A c, a, b

2B 1 by saying
2 main reasons
3 As a result
4 led to
5 impact of this

PRONUNCIATION
3A 1 I'd like to start off by <u>saying</u> / that I <u>completely agree</u> / that social <u>media</u> / has <u>killed</u> the art of conversation.
2 <u>Firstly</u>, / we no longer have to interact <u>face</u> to face / with people who <u>disagree</u> with us.
3 <u>Secondly</u>, / whereas in the <u>past</u> / we had to <u>call</u> or <u>arrange</u> to <u>meet</u> someone we hadn't <u>spoken</u> to in a long <u>while</u>, / now we can just <u>fire</u> off a quick message <u>online</u>.

SPEAKING
4A 1 start
2 evidence
3 example
4 impact
5 point
6 true
7 Firstly
8 secondly

Lesson 8D
VOCABULARY
1A 1 c 2 e 3 d 4 a 5 f 6 b

1B 1 got a big heart
2 get somewhere to live
3 get to the other side
4 get your confidence back
5 get your life back together
6 get out

READING
2A 1 homelessness
2 climate change
3 endangered languages
4 lack of affordable housing
5 literacy

2B 1 washing machines
2 bicycles
3 over 700
4 design and build
5 self-esteem

REVIEW 7–8
GRAMMAR
1 1 a 2 b 3 a 4 b 5 a 6 c

2 1 had
2 had told
3 have practised
4 wouldn't/didn't bark
5 could/would visit
6 shouldn't have taken

3 1 e 2 b 3 d 4 a 5 c

4 1 Arriving in the capital, many young people struggle to find work.
2 Having moved to the city, Miguel was surprised by how noisy it was.
3 Having finally finished the report, Sally left work on time for once.
4 Being brought up with much older siblings, Teddy grew up really fast.
5 Spending so many hours in the gym, Tina was always too tired to walk home.

5 1 on condition (that) you only stay
2 in conversation unless
3 and meet you providing (that)
4 go well as long as
5 couple of hours provided (that)

VOCABULARY
6 1 nineteen-year-old
2 by chance
3 life-changing
4 fortunate
5 all-consuming
6 world-famous

7 1 not my cup of tea
2 a blessing in disguise
3 back to the drawing board
4 was a piece of cake
5 missed the boat
6 the grass is always greener on the other side

8 1 down
2 into
3 down
4 over/through
5 through/over
6 across
7 out
8 out

9 1 went
2 went
3 make
4 made
5 made
6 had

10 1 exclusive
2 secure
3 spacious
4 elegant
5 character

11 1 b 2 d 3 f 4 a 5 e 6 c

ANSWER KEY

12
1. by far
2. on the whole
3. at the same time
4. out of control
5. At least
6. in order to

13 1 a 2 c 3 c 4 a 5 b 6 c

CUMULATIVE REVIEW 1–4

GRAMMAR

1
1. How long have you been learning the violin?
2. Have you ever been to Russia?
3. I've been going to bed much later recently.
4. I've been waiting here for the last two and half hours!
5. Ali has seen the new *James Bond* film three times.

2
1. buying
2. to invite
3. waking
4. practising
5. to travel

3
1. 'll
2. unlikely to
3. might
4. going to
5. certain to

4
1. where
2. –
3. whose
4. which/that
5. –

5
1. It was
2. What was / What is
3. What
4. was
5. It was
6. what's

6
1. have finished
2. be working
3. have finished
4. have spoken
5. have finalised

VOCABULARY

7
1. stubborn
2. curious
3. adventurous
4. ambitious
5. argumentative

8
1. practical
2. experienced
3. relaxed
4. reliable
5. optimistic
6. realistic

9
1. virtual reality
2. smart
3. findings
4. analyse
5. remotely

10
1. transform
2. keep/stay
3. stay/keep
4. do
5. expand
6. keep

11
1. unique
2. modest
3. ordinary
4. tedious
5. harsh

12
1. organisers
2. carbon footprint
3. attracts
4. festival-goers
5. renewable
6. venues
7. acts
8. sustainable

HOW TO …

13
1. about
2. fan
3. not
4. into
5. What
6. be

14
1. thought
2. impression
3. sure
4. way
5. fact

15
1. so
2. of
3. stuff
4. and
5. kind/sort
6. or

CUMULATIVE REVIEW 5–8

GRAMMAR

1
1. had eaten
2. had left
3. had been doing
4. had been ringing
5. had always loved

2
1. was supposed to see
2. was going to go
3. was considering getting
4. was expecting to see
5. were planning to go

3
1. had to
2. permitted
3. couldn't
4. allowed
5. must

4
1. can't have been
2. must have been
3. might (always) have had
4. must have decided
5. couldn't have travelled

ANSWER KEY

5 1 we'd left
   2 have told
   3 I'd tried
   4 had told
   5 they'd be

6 1 Waking
   2 Climbing
   3 unlocked
   4 Sitting
   5 Having

VOCABULARY

7 1 accountancy
   2 retrain
   3 started out
   4 advancing
   5 publishing

8 1 impatient
   2 rewritten
   3 subheading
   4 dishonest
   5 misunderstood

9 1 suggested
   2 denied
   3 insisted
   4 refused
   5 regret

10 1 world-famous
    2 widely respected
    3 time-consuming
    4 life-changing
    5 long-lasting
    6 fifty-eight-year-old

11 1 random
    2 unfortunate
    3 unexpected
    4 by chance
    5 fortunate

12 1 get, across
    2 figure, out
    3 leave out
    4 talk, through
    5 go over

13 1 secure
    2 character
    3 spacious
    4 exclusive
    5 condition

14 1 endangered
    2 literacy
    3 housing
    4 homeless
    5 poverty

HOW TO …

15 1 get
    2 wrong
    3 problem
    4 worth
    5 Why
    6 might

16 1 advice
    2 hope
    3 suggest
    4 might
    5 should

17 1 begin
    2 step
    3 you've
    4 It's
    5 be
    6 want
    7 stage

CUMULATIVE REVIEW 1–8

GRAMMAR

1 1 h **2** b **3** a **4** e **5** f **6** c **7** d **8** g

2 1 few
   2 handful
   3 majority
   4 good
   5 all
   6 number
   7 each
   8 little

3 1 did used to like
   2 do really like this song
   3 of concerts, but I do
   4 don't still work at
   5 do want to go

4 1 is, accepted
   2 are expected
   3 is recommended
   4 was thought
   5 was believed
   6 has been reported
   7 was decided
   8 is suggested / has been suggested

5 1 which was a surprise.
   2 which is a relief
   3 who I get on well with
   4 which was extremely boring
   5 which was annoying
   6 which seems unfair
   7 which is great to hear
   8 who he enjoys being taught by

6 1 said, looked
   2 advised, was
   3 warned, were
   4 recommended being
   5 suggested following
   6 wished

7 1 However
   2 Although
   3 Though
   4 although
   5 Although
   6 Though
   7 Though
   8 However

ANSWER KEY

8
1. on condition (that) they are over one metre tall.
2. Your lunch will go cold unless you
3. I'll go with you to the concert provided (that) we don't stand
4. as long as we leave right now
5. So long as you are home by ten o'clock,

HOW TO …

9
1. point
2. fair/good
3. hand
4. mean
5. take/see

10 e, c, d, a, b

VOCABULARY

1
1. ear
2. recall
3. memories
4. detail
5. heart
6. mind
7. tricks

2
1. about
2. of
3. of
4. on
5. of

3
1. research
2. prediction
3. virtual
4. remotely
5. analytically
6. scientist

4
1. coastline
2. woodland
3. track
4. deserted beach
5. river bank

5 1 f 2 a 3 d 4 c 5 b 6 e

6
1. came
2. carry
3. messed
4. live
5. came
6. put

7
1. soundtrack
2. subtitles
3. cast
4. twist
5. based
6. ending

8 1 b 2 c 3 a 4 c 5 b

9
1. benefits
2. sleep
3. high-impact, exhausted
4. challenge
5. moderate

10
1. time
2. threat
3. moment
4. time
5. opportunity

11
1. internet connection
2. frozen
3. host
4. invite
5. echo
6. delay

12
1. got
2. take
3. got
4. take
5. got

13 1 d 2 c 3 a 4 e 5 b

14
1. made
2. have
3. make
4. go
5. went

15
1. In order to
2. on the whole
3. By far
4. At least
5. out of control